STUDENT ACTIVITIES IN

UNITED STATES HISTORY

for Christian Schools®

Terri L. Koontz
Lynn Garland

Bob Jones University Press
Greenville, South Carolina 29614

TEACHER'S EDITION

Photograph Credits
The following agencies and individuals have furnished materials to meet the photographic needs of this textbook. We wish to express our gratitude to them for their important contribution.

DigitalSTOCK
International Herald Tribune, The
Library of Congress

Oxford University Press
PhotoDisc, Inc.
Unusual Films

Cover
Unusual Films (Front left, spine, back)
DigitalSTOCK (Front right)

PhotoDisc, Inc. 21; Unusual Films 35; Library of Congress LC-USZ62-056944 53 (left), LC-USZ62-121242 53 (right); Oxford University Press 76; International Herald Tribune, The 103

NOTE:
The fact that materials produced by other publishers are referred to in this volume does not constitute an endorsement by Bob Jones University Press of the content or theological position of materials produced by such publishers. The position of Bob Jones University Press, and the University itself, is well known. Any references and ancillary materials are listed as an aid to the student or the teacher and in an attempt to maintain the accepted academic standards of the publishing industry.

Student Activities in UNITED STATES HISTORY for Christian Schools®
Teacher's Edition

For use with UNITED STATES HISTORY for Christian Schools,® Third Edition

Terri Koontz
Lynn Garland

Compositor
Kelley Moore

Cover and Design
Joseph Tyrpak

Illustrators
Jim Hargis
Kathy Pflug

Project Editor
Manda Kalagayan

Produced in cooperation with the Bob Jones University Department of History of the College of Arts and Science, the School of Religion, and Bob Jones Academy.

for Christian Schools is a registered trademark of Bob Jones University Press.

© 1993, 2001 Bob Jones University Press
Greenville, South Carolina 29614
First Edition © 1993 Bob Jones University Press

ISBN 1-57924-643-5

15 14 13 12 11 10 9 8 7 6 5 4 3 2 1

CONTENTS

Unit V: Quest

Unit VI: Leadership

Unit VII: Challenge

How to Use the Activities Manual

These activities are designed to give you maximum flexibility. We have provided a "menu" of activities from which you can select the ones that will help you achieve your instructional goals. Before you begin each chapter, look over the activities and decide how you want to assign them. The activity codes and skill codes at the bottom of each activity will help you decide.

Activity Codes

Each chapter has four to six activities. The activity code tells you which sections of the chapter each activity covers. The code also tells you whether the activity is good for reinforcement, enrichment, or review.

- Reinforcement activities are based solely on the information in the textbook. They help students (1) to recognize and recall major terms and concepts in the chapter and (2) to "put it all together." Some reinforcement activities, such as charts and time lines, cover the entire chapter. (Students can complete them as they read through the chapter or as they review for tests.) Other reinforcement activities apply to a specific section of the chapter. (Students can complete them as they read the section.)

- Enrichment activities go beyond the textbook. They help students (1) to apply information from the chapter, (2) to pursue subjects they find interesting, and (3) to develop special skills. Every student can benefit from these activities, but they are particularly useful for students who need a challenge. Most enrichment activities are related to a specific section in the chapter.

- Chapter review activities help students to prepare for the chapter test. They include crossword puzzles, games, and other interesting activities that review the chapter.

Alternative Uses of the Activities

Activities are useful for more than just homework. You can make them an integral part of your classroom discussion. Your students will especially appreciate your help in completing the more difficult activities.

- Homework—The students complete the activity at home.

- Class activity—The students complete the activity in class by themselves or in groups.

- Class discussion—You help the class complete the activity together in a classroom discussion.

- Lecture—You complete the activity on the chalkboard or overhead projector during your lecture, while the students take notes.

- Game—The students answer each question in a competition that pits team against team or "every man for himself."

Skill Codes

Every activity focuses on one of eighteen skills that history students need to learn. Some activities teach specific skills, such as mapping. Others teach basic thinking skills, such as recognizing terms. The activities for each skill increase in variety and difficulty over the year. *Note: Each number in the chart below corresponds to the activity number for that chapter.*

Chapter	1	2	3	4	5	6	7	8	9	10	11	12	13	14	15	16	17	18	19	20	21	22	23	24	25	26	27
1. Maps	2	3		1	2	3	1		2, 4	1	1	5					1	4	3			2, 3	2	2		1, 4	
2. Charts						3		4			4	2, 5	2			3	5, 6	4	2	4					2		1, 4
3. Outlining														4													
4. Time Line	6			3	1				2			3					5						5				
5. Graphs																2, 3											
6. Original Sources		1, 2				5						4							1	4							
7. Cause and Effect	1																	2									
8. Using Resources	1	4	2		2		1	1	1		1		1	1	2	3		4	2		1						
9. Bible Study	3												1						4				4	3	1		
10. Writing		4					4		6			2		5	4												
11. Vocabulary			3																								
12. Test-taking		5		2		4				3	4								5			4	6			3	
13. Recognition	5		1, 4	4	1, 4				3	4			4					3		6	2				4		5
14. Comprehension			3					2, 3	5, 3		3		3					5		4							2
15. Application	4				3		3								2	4		1		3				1		2	
16. Analysis								1					1	2	3, 5	1	4		2	1			3		3	5	3, 6
17. Synthesis							2									3											4
18. Evaluation						2					2			3	5				3	1			1		1	5	

Alternatives to Grading and Burdensome Records

You don't need to grade all the activities. You can complete some of them in class discussions, games, and lectures, as mentioned above. Or you can use some of the ideas below.

- Check marks—Give simple pluses and minuses. You can use this information to decide borderline grades or—if you use them—"effort" grades.

- Extra credit—Let students do activities for extra credit, if they wish.

- Sporadic grades—Grade every third or fourth activity, but do not let students know which activities will be graded.

- Notebook—Make students keep their activities in a notebook. Collect the notebooks quarterly and grade them for neatness, completeness, and accuracy.

Think About It!

Use a dictionary or an encyclopedia to help you answer these questions.

The Indians had a custom called "potlatch" in which they would give a dinner and gifts to visitors. They did this expecting gifts in return. How do you think confusion about this custom could have caused tension between the Indians and the explorers?

The students should realize that the explorers could have understood the gifts to have been

given in homage or worship of the explorers. This would have made the Europeans feel superior

and overly confident of the natives' good will. The students should also see that the natives would

have taken offense when gifts were not given in return and, in contrast, the Europeans expected

and took more from them.

For almost two hundred years the Europeans went on Crusades to rid the Holy Land of "infidels." How did this practice eventually lead to the discovery and exploration of the New World, and how did it affect the treatment of the people they found there?

The students should understand that the Crusades opened the eyes of Europe to spices, fabric,

and other goods available in the East. When the normal trade routes were closed to them, they

explored new ways to get to the products desired. The students should remember that during the

Crusades, the Europeans killed the "infidels" for being non-Christian, so it became easier to kill

the heathen that they found in the New World.

The Micmac Indians of Canada normally used what they needed from the land and left the rest. After the arrival of the French, however, the Indians began to deplete the beaver population to near extinction in their area. What caused them to change their normal way of hunting?

A small amount of research will reveal to the students that the Indians lived in small tribes that

did not interact. Without intertribal trading, there was no reason to use more from their surround-

ings than the tribe needed at the time. However, when the French arrived on Indian soil, they

brought an endless demand for pelts of all kinds. Natural human greed took over, and the Indians

killed as many beavers as they could find.

ENRICHMENT: Section I   SKILLS: Cause and Effect and Using Resources   1

Map Study: Explorations of the New World

Refer to the map on page 5 and the text.

In the blank to the left of the explorer's name, write the letter from the map below that corresponds to the route that explorer took on his travels. In the blank to the right of his name, write the name of the country for which he explored and the year he began his exploration.

___E___ 1. Cabot   _____ England 1497 _____

___A___ 2. Columbus   _____ Spain 1492 _____

___C___ 3. Coronado   _____ Spain 1540 _____

___G___ 4. Cortés   _____ Spain 1519 _____

___D___ 5. De Soto   _____ Spain 1539 _____

___B___ 6. Drake   _____ England 1577 (Beginning date as on text page 11) _____

___F___ 7. Magellan   _____ Spain 1519 (Beginning date as on text page 5) _____

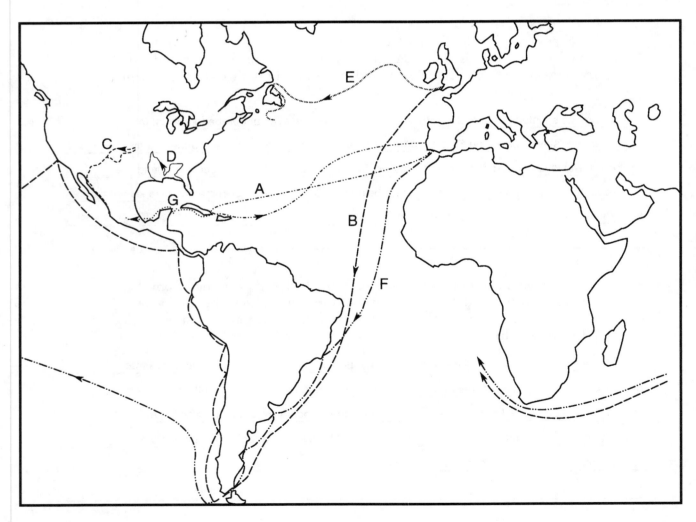

Read and Heed

The early Virginia settlers came to America with dreams of prosperity and wealth. They had heard of the Spanish conquest of South America's gold and silver and of the Indian laborers to be had. When they arrived in America, they found life much more difficult than they expected. Rather than working hard to become self-sufficient, the colonists chose to work about four hours a day and relax and entertain themselves the rest of the time. After a winter in which sixty out of one hundred colonists died, Captain John Smith took charge and enforced with punishment the biblical rule "if any would not work, neither should he eat" (II Thess. 3:10).

Find eight other verses that warn about laziness. Write the reference and the principle for living found there.

	REFERENCE	LIFE PRINCIPLE
		(Students' answers will vary.)
1.	Colossians 3:23-24	Do your work with the greatest effort to please God since He is the one from whom your ultimate reward will come.
2.	Proverbs 24:30-32	The slothful man will be unproductive; and, if he does change his ways, it will be more difficult for him to get back on track.
3.	II Peter 3:14	God commands us to be diligent in our Christian service so that we will be doing right when He returns.
4.	Proverbs 13:4	The lazy man wants things but isn't willing to work for them. The diligent man has things because he has worked for them.
5.	Proverbs 10:26	If you are lazy and won't do what you should, you will be an irritation to those in authority over you.
6.	Proverbs 22:29	Diligence will most likely be rewarded with greater responsibility as well as greater position.
7.	Ecclesiastes 9:10	Work to the best of your ability while you have time because death comes soon and there will be no more time to work.
8.	Proverbs 20:4	Don't let situations that seem too hard stop you from accomplishing the tasks that need to be done.

Who Am I?

Read each statement and decide who would have said it. Write the correct answer in the blank.

_____Rustichello_____ 1. I wrote a travel-log of a famous explorer with whom I shared a prison cell.

Ferdinand Magellan 2. I set sail from Spain with three hundred men and five ships. Three years later, one of my ships arrived home with only eighteen original crew members left.

Hernando Cortés 3. I disobeyed the governor of Cuba and conquered the richest Indian tribe in Mexico.

Marco Polo 4. I told of my adventures in China and of a land called Cipangu, which was reportedly paved with gold.

John Cabot 5. I, Giovanni, reached Newfoundland in search of China. To the English, I was known by a different name.

Christopher Columbus 6. My calculations were faulty, but I thought I could sail three thousand miles west to reach China.

Martin Luther 7. Romans 1:17 ("The just shall live by faith") transformed my life and teachings.

Sir Francis Drake 8. In my ship, *The Golden Hind*, I fought the Catholic threat on the high seas with my cousin Sir John Hawkins.

Captain John Smith 9. Second Thessalonians 3:10 ("If any would not work, neither should he eat") was a verse I enforced to ensure Jamestown's survival.

Ponce de León 10. In a Spanish attempt to settle the southeastern United States, I was the first to explore the Florida peninsula in 1513.

Amerigo Vespucci 11. A German mapmaker named the New World after me instead of after Columbus.

Francisco de Coronado 12. I searched for the Seven Cities of Cibola and found the Grand Canyon.

Vasco da Gama 13. A cargo of spices worth sixty times the cost of my expedition was my reward for sailing to India.

Sir Walter Raleigh 14. I financed two attempts to colonize the New World in an area that I called Virginia.

Hernando de Soto 15. I landed at Tampa Bay, traveled to North Carolina, and eventually discovered the Mississippi River.

John Rolfe 16. I helped bring peace to Jamestown by marrying an Indian chief's daughter.

Governor John White 17. I went to England for supplies, and when I returned, I found the town of Raleigh empty.

Bartolomeu Dias 18. I was the first to round the southern cape of Africa.

The New World

Read each question carefully. Write the answers in the blanks and then unscramble the numbered letters to find the mystery word.

1. Promoters tried to attract settlers to Virginia by calling it

   N O V A   B R I T A N N I A.
                1

2. A movement that rediscovered biblical truth and shattered the religious monopoly of Rome was known as the

   R E F O R M A T I O N.
          2

3. Unfortunately, this king lured the Spanish to conquer his kingdom by offering rich farewell gifts.

   M O N T E Z U M A
         3

4. What was the nickname Queen Elizabeth I gave to John Hawkins and Francis Drake?

   S E A   D O G S
       4

5. Who was the explorer for whom the New World was named?

   A M E R I G O   V E S P U C C I
           5

6. What is the name of the company that made only one attempt to colonize Maine?

   P L Y M O U T H   C O M P A N Y
         6

7. The large force of Spanish ships that attempted to conquer England was called the

   S P A N I S H   A R M A D A.
             7

8. What was the name Columbus gave the island on which he landed?

   S A N   S A L V A D O R
     8

9. The Indian nation which was conquered by Cortés was the

   A Z T E C S.
       9

MYSTERY WORD

The New World promised wealth, freedom, and

   A D V E N T U R E.

What Comes Next?

Place the following events in their correct order using the spaces provided below.

A. Jamestown—first permanent English settlement
B. Beginning of Protestant Reformation with Martin Luther
C. Dias sails along African coast and names the southern cape Good Hope
D. Ponce de León explores the Florida peninsula
E. Virginia House of Burgesses is established
F. Cabot's sail to Newfoundland establishes English North American claims
G. Hernando Cortés conquers Aztec city of Tenochtitlán
H. Roanoke Island (Lost Colony)
I. Rustichello writes of Marco Polo's experiences
J. Vasco da Gama sails to India and returns with expensive spice cargo
K. Spanish Armada is launched against England
L. Christopher Columbus discovers New World
M. Sir Francis Drake begins world voyage
N. Magellan begins his voyage around the Earth

1. I—Rustichello writes of Marco Polo's experiences
2. C—Dias sails along African coast and names the southern cape Good Hope
3. L—Christopher Columbus discovers the New World
4. F—Cabot's sail to Newfoundland establishes English North American claims
5. J—Vasco da Gama sails to India and returns with expensive spice cargo
6. D—Ponce de León explores the Florida peninsula
7. B—Beginning of Protestant Reformation with Martin Luther
8. N—Magellan begins his voyage around the Earth
9. G—Hernando Cortés conquers Aztec city of Tenochtitlán
10. M—Sir Francis Drake begins world voyage
11. H—Roanoke Island (Lost Colony)
12. K—Spanish Armada is launched against England
13. A—Jamestown—first permanent English settlement
14. E—Virginia House of Burgesses is established

Providence Praised

Read this excerpt from William Bradford's *Of Plymouth Plantation* and then answer the questions on the next page.

Having found a good haven and being brought safely in sight of land, they fell upon their knees and blessed the God of Heaven who had brought them over the vast and furious ocean, and delivered them from all the peril and miseries of it, again to set their feet upon the firm and stable earth, their proper element.

But here I cannot but make a pause, and stand half amazed at this poor people's present condition; and so I think will the reader, too, when he considers it well. Having thus passed the vast ocean, and that sea of troubles before while they were making their preparations, they now had no friends to welcome them, nor inns to entertain and refresh their weather-beaten bodies, nor houses—much less towns—to repair to.

It is recorded in Scripture (Acts, xxviii) as a mercy to the Apostle and his shipwrecked crew, that the barbarians showed them no small kindness in refreshing them; but these savage barbarians when they met with them were readier to fill their sides full of arrows than otherwise! As for the season, it was winter, and those who have experienced the winters of the country know them to be sharp and severe, and subject to fierce storms when it is dangerous to travel to known places—much more to search an unknown coast. Besides, what could they see but a desolate wilderness, full of wild beasts and wild men; and what multitude there might be of them they knew not! Neither could they, as it were, go up to the top of Pisgah, to view from this wilderness a more goodly country to feed their hopes; for which way soever they turned their eyes (save upward to the heavens!) they could gain little solace from any outward objects. Summer being done, all things turned upon them a weatherbeaten face; and the whole country, full of woods and thickets, presented a wild and savage view.

If they looked behind them, there was the mighty ocean which they had passed, and was now a gulf separating them from all civilized parts of the world. If it be said that they had their ship to turn to, it is true; but what did they hear daily from the captain and crew. That they should quickly look out for a place with their shallop, where they would be not far off; for the season was such that the captain would not approach nearer to the shore till a harbor had been discovered which he could enter safely; and that the food was being consumed apace, but he must and would keep sufficient for the return voyage. It was even muttered by some of the crew that if they did not find a place in time, they would turn them and their goods ashore and leave them.

Let it be remembered, too, what small hope of further assistance from England they had left behind them, to support their courage in this sad condition and the trials they were under; for how the case stood between the settlers and the merchants at their departure has already been described. It is true, indeed, that the affection and love of their brethren at Leyden towards them was cordial and unbroken; but they had little power to help them or themselves.

What, then, could now sustain them but the spirit of God, and His grace? Ought not the children of their fathers rightly to say: Our fathers were Englishmen who came over the great ocean, and were ready to perish in this wilderness; but they cried unto the Lord, and He heard their voice, and looked on their adversity. . . . Let them therefore praise the Lord, because He is good, and His mercies endure forever. Yea, let them that have been redeemed of the Lord, show how He hath delivered them from the hand of the oppressor. When they wandered forth into the desert wilderness, out of the way, and found no city to dwell in, both hungry and thirsty, their soul was overwhelmed in them. Let them confess before the Lord His loving kindness, and His wonderful works before the sons of men!

1. Look up and define the following words.

   shallop _an open boat fitted with oars or sails or both_

   apace _at a rapid pace, swiftly_

2. Look up Deuteronomy 34:1. How does the reference to Mt. Pisgah fit with the allusion in paragraph three? _Moses went up Mt. Pisgah to view all of the Promised Land. The_ _settlers needed a place to stand to view all of their "promised land."_

3. After reading paragraph four, how would you describe the captain's and crew's feelings toward the Pilgrims? _They were more concerned with getting back to England with_ _enough food than they were with helping the Pilgrims. It was probably strictly a business deal._

4. What feelings (implied in paragraph five) were between the settlers and merchants when the Pilgrims left England? _The paragraph implies that the settlers left England with bad_ _feelings between them and the merchants who had outfitted them for the endeavor._

5. For extra credit, identify the psalm that Bradford paraphrases in the final paragraph. _He paraphrases Psalm 107._

6. Write a first-person narrative paragraph about your first impressions and hopes for the new land. Write from the perspective of Joseph or Priscilla Mullins, two children who came over on the *Mayflower* with their parents.

Mayflower Compact Impact

Read the Mayflower Compact below and compare it with the Preamble of the U.S. Constitution, which can be found on page 662 of the textbook.

In the name of God, Amen. We, whose names are underwritten, the loyal subjects of our dread sovereigne Lord, King James, by the grace of God, of Great Britaine, France, and Ireland king, defender of the faith, etc., having undertaken, for the glory of God, and advancement of the Christian faith, and honour of our king and country, a voyage to plant the first colony in the Northerne parts of Virginia, doe, by these presents solemnly and mutually in the presence of God, and one of another, covenant and combine ourselves together into a civill body politick, for our better ordering and preservation and furtherance of the ends aforesaid; and by virtue hereof to enacte, constitute, and frame such just and equall laws, ordinances, acts, constitutions, and offices, from time to time, as shall be thought most meete and convenient for the generall good of the Colonie unto which we promise all due submission and obedience. In witness whereof we have hereunder subscribed our names at Cap-Codd the 11 of November, in the year of the raigne of our sovereigne lord, King James, of England, France, and Ireland, the eighteenth, and of Scotland the fifte-fourth. Anno. Dom. 1620.

1. What is the significance of the Mayflower Compact to the United States government as a whole? _The Mayflower Compact was a first step toward creating a government based upon_ _the consent of those being governed._ _____

2. Compare the similarities of the Mayflower Compact and the Constitution Preamble.

Mayflower Compact	*Constitution Preamble*
a) _We ... loyal subjects of ..._	We the people of the United States
b) _combine...together...civill body politick_	to form a more perfect union
c) _frame such just and equall laws_	establish justice
d) _convenient for the generall good of the Colonie_	promote the general welfare

Map Study: Settlement of the Colonies

Refer to the maps on pages 21, 28, and 30 as well as an atlas and the text to complete the map below.

1. Label each of the original thirteen colonies with the complete name of the colony.
2. Identify the New England Colonies, including the disputed territory; the Middle Colonies; and the Southern Colonies. Color each section a different color and make a key to fit your colors.
3. Label the following settlements by placing a small dot on the map and then writing the name of the settlement beside the dot.
   - Baltimore
   - Boston
   - Charleston
   - Jamestown
   - New York City
   - Philadelphia
4. Below the colony names, write the name(s) of the founder(s).

   A. New Hampshire

   _____David Thomson_____

   _____John Wheelwright_____

   B. Massachusetts

   _____William Bradford_____

   _____John Winthrop_____

   C. Connecticut

   _____Thomas Hooker_____

   D. Rhode Island

   _____Roger Williams_____

   _____Anne Hutchinson_____

   E. New York

   _____Henry Hudson_____

   _____Peter Minuit_____

   _____Peter Stuyvesant_____

   F. Pennsylvania

   _____William Penn_____

   G. Maryland

   _____Cecilius Calvert_____

   _____Lord Baltimore_____

   H. The Carolinas

   _____Sir Anthony Cooper_____

   I. Georgia

   _____James Oglethorpe_____

NEW YORK

NEW HAMPSHIRE

Boston

New York City

PENNSYLVANIA

MASSACHUSETTS

RHODE ISLAND

Philadelphia

CONNECTICUT

NEW JERSEY

DELAWARE

MARYLAND

Baltimore

VIRGINIA

Jamestown

NORTH CAROLINA

SOUTH CAROLINA

GEORGIA

Charleston

NEW ENGLAND COLONIES

MIDDLE COLONIES

SOUTHERN COLONIES

Choices, Choices

Choose one of the original colonies. Research its history and complete the following activity based upon the information obtained. Students' answers will vary.

1. Colony name ————————————————————————

2. Climate type ————————————————————————

3. Main income source in the colony ———————————————————

4. Common foods that would have been grown and eaten ————————————

   ———————————————————————————————————

5. Occupation best suited to the colony ————————————————————

6. List five items that you would have wanted to bring with you to the colony and tell
   why they would have been important. ———————————————————

   ———————————————————————————————————

   ———————————————————————————————————

   ———————————————————————————————————

   ———————————————————————————————————

   ———————————————————————————————————

7. Write a letter to your parents in England telling them why your choice to come to
   this colony was a good one and telling them what problems you have encountered.

   ———————————————————————————————————

   ———————————————————————————————————

   ———————————————————————————————————

   ———————————————————————————————————

   ———————————————————————————————————

   ———————————————————————————————————

   ———————————————————————————————————

   ———————————————————————————————————

   ———————————————————————————————————

   ———————————————————————————————————

   ———————————————————————————————————

   ———————————————————————————————————

   ———————————————————————————————————

Colonial Order

Put the correct letter in the blank provided.

___D___ 1. A colony that was governed by a trade company was a
A. royal colony.   C. trade colony.
B. proprietary colony.   D. charter colony.

___A___ 2. An indenture was
A. a work contract.   C. a set of wooden false teeth.
B. a fifty-acre land tract.   D. a servant.

___C___ 3. The belief that outward obedience to the Scripture was unnecessary to show
an inner relationship to Christ was called
A. Fundamental Orders.   C. Antinomianism.
B. Concessions and Agreements.   D. Predestination.

___A___ 4. "Precious stink" was a description of America's first cash crop.
A. tobacco   C. cabbage
B. cauliflower   D. corn

___B___ 5. "Holy Experiment" refers to the state of
A. Delaware.   C. Maryland.
B. Pennsylvania.   D. New York.

___D___ 6. If someone paid for his passage to the New World, the Virginia Company
offered him
A. a patroon.   C. a work contract.
B. an indenture.   D. headrights.

___B___ 7. The group of settlers who came from Scrooby, England, then moved to
Holland, and finally settled in Massachusetts was called the
A. Anglicans.   C. Puritans.
B. Separatists.   D. fundamentalists.

___D___ 8. The man who dreamed of a "wilderness Zion" in Massachusetts was
A. William Bradford.   C. Roger Williams.
B. Thomas Hooker.   D. John Winthrop.

___A___ 9. This document has been called the first written constitution in America.
A. Fundamental Orders of Connecticut   C. Mayflower Compact
B. Law, Concessions, and Agreements   D. Toleration Act of 1649

___A___ 10. The man who discovered a waterway from below Long Island to Albany,
New York, was
A. Henry Hudson.   C. Peter Minuit.
B. Peter Stuyvesant.   D. Cecilius Calvert.

___C___ 11. Thomas Hooker moved three congregations into the Connecticut River valley
to form what was collectively called the
A. Massachusetts Bay Company.   C. River Colony.
B. Puritan Plurality.   D. Mystic River Towns.

___B___ 12. The contract of government drawn up by those on the *Mayflower* was known
as the
A. Plymouth Plan.   C. Articles of Agreement.
B. Mayflower Compact.   D. Separatist Doctrine.

Eastern Indian Tribes

Choose one of the following Eastern Indian tribes. Using outside resources, answer the following questions about the chosen tribe. The activity could be used in a class discussion. Answers will vary.

Cherokee	Alabama	Algonquin	Delaware	Erie
Fox	Chickasaw	Creek	Iowa	Menominee
Miami	Huron	Illinois	Ojibwa	Osage
Missouri	Sauk	Mohican	Powhatan	Potawatomi
Ottawa	Yamasee	Natchez	Catawba	Susquehanna
Quapaw	Shawnee			

1. Where in the Eastern United States was the tribe located? _____
_____

2. What are some interesting facts about the tribe's culture? _____
_____
_____
_____

3. What type of government did the tribe have? _____
_____
_____

4. What is the earliest known contact between the tribe and Europeans? _____
_____
_____

5. Were there any well-known members of the tribe? If so, who were they, and why were they well known? _____
_____
_____

6. Were there any unique facts about the tribe not previously known? _____
_____
_____

7. Are members of this tribe living today, and if so where? _____
_____
_____
_____

Native Americans

Put the correct answers in the blanks provided.

1. What two major groups of Mound Builders lived in North America? _temple and burial_

   _____

2. List one effigy mound and one fortification mound. _Adena Serpent Mound (effigy)_
   Fort Ancient (fortification)

3. What were the six tribes who joined together to form the Iroquois Confederacy?
   Seneca, Cayuga, Onondaga, Oneida, Mohawk, Tuscarora

   _____

4. Who persuaded the tribes to come together in peace? _Deganwidah persuaded the Iroquois_
   to come together in a peace he called "the tree of the Great Peace."

   _____

5. What were the chiefs called? _sachems_

6. Who ruled over the longhouse? _a woman (usually the oldest among the families)_

   _____

7. What native crop discovered by Columbus has become one of the four most important foods in the world? _corn_

8. How did the Indians clear the land of trees? _The Indians cleared the land by girdling the_
   trees and then burning them and the surrounding ground cover.

   _____

9. What did some tribes use as a scarecrow? _Some tribes would place someone (often a young_
   child) in a shelter in the middle of the field.

   _____

10. How did the Indians' corn differ from today's corn and why? _Wild corn was smaller and_
    produced fewer kernels. Crossbreeding and hybridization have made the corn of today much larger
    and fuller than Indian corn.

    _____

Who and What

Use complete sentences to answer the following who or what questions.

1. What group of people did Benjamin Franklin refer to as "aliens"?

   The "aliens" to which he referred were the Germans, or Pennsylvania Dutch.

2. What Iroquois Indian trail did the early settlers use to migrate to the South?

   The old Indian trail was called the Great Philadelphia Wagon Road.

3. What were two epidemics that seriously reduced the New England population?

   The two epidemics were smallpox and infectious dysentery.

4. Who was the Puritan pastor who promoted inoculation to prevent disease?

   Reverend Cotton Mather tried to convince people to be inoculated.

5. What toy reflected the high mortality rate among colonial children?

   Death was so common that some homemade dolls came with their own coffins.

6. From what is colonial architectural style copied?

   Colonial architectural style copied the English Tudor style.

7. What was the paddle-shaped board used as a child's first book?

   The hornbook was usually a child's first book.

8. From what did it (#7) get its name?

   The hornbook got its name because its surface was covered with a thin layer of horn.

9. From what text is "In Adam's fall, we sinned all" taken?

   This text is taken from the *New England Primer*.

10. What was a school taught by a widow or a spinster?

    A school taught by a widow or a spinster was called a dame school.

11. What was the 1769 New York advertisement talking about when it said it "saved many from drowning"?

    The New York advertisement was talking about the cork life jacket.

12. What staple food, first discovered in Peru, went to Europe and came back to North America in the 1700s?

    The staple food mentioned here was the potato.

13. What was the purpose of education in the 1700s?

    The purpose of education was to provide basic skills and the ability to read the Bible.

The Servant and the Slave

Use the text and an encyclopedia to help you compare and contrast the life of an indentured servant and that of a slave.

Students' answers may vary.

SERVANT		SLAVE
Families were sometimes left intact, but family members would often be separated. Family members may have been able to reunite after their contract was finished, or they may have lost contact altogether.	Family Life	Families were often separated by no choice of their own. They had very little opportunity to be reunited.
Treatment depended entirely on the temperament of the person who had paid the indenture costs. Some masters were kind; others were cruel.	Treatment	Treatment also depended on the master's temperament. More expensive slaves or slaves who could do a specific task, such as a blacksmith, may have gotten better treatment based on their value.
Indentured servants were not usually allowed to marry during their indentured time. Their masters wanted their undivided attention.	Social Life	Slaves from a given farm were allowed to mingle among themselves after work hours were over. They sometimes had their own religious services. Their masters often chose their mates.
A male indentured servant was purchased to do much of the hard labor. The women did household chores and sometimes harvested in the fields. Some servants were apprenticed for a particular craft.	Work	Black slaves were often expected to endure the heat better than whites and would have to spend more hours in the field. Unless they had a special skill, they did hard labor.
The indentured servant always had before him the promise of a contract honored and time fulfilled. He knew when he started work that, no matter how bad things were, his service would be over in a set number of years.	Future Prospects	Unless they had a kind master, slaves had very little to look forward to. Their purchase was for life, and rarely were they granted their freedom. They could plan to live and die on the same farm.

False Alarms

Circle the appropriate letter to identify the statement as true or false. If the statement is false, correct it.

(T) F   1. Malaria claimed lives in South Carolina in the early colonial days.

_____

T (F) 2. A subsistence crop is a crop produced to raise money.

Change subsistence to cash OR A subsistence crop is raised to feed the farmer's family.

T (F) 3. A pennysheet was paper money equivalent to a penny.

A pennysheet was a page from a book such as *Poor Richard's Almanack*.

(T) F   4. Passage to the New World was sometimes paid for by indenture.

_____

T (F) 5. Linsey-woolsey was the fuzz that collected when the women wove cloth.

Linsey-woolsey was the name for a woven mixture of linen and wool.

(T) F   6. If your fire went out, you could borrow a "chunk of fire."

_____

T (F) 7. Wigs were popular only with bald men.

Wigs were popular with men who could afford them for style, whether they were bald or not.

T (F) 8. The "bagwig" was carried in a linen bag for emergency use.

A "bagwig" was a wig with the long tresses held in a silk pouch.

T (F) 9. A wig was "dressed" with ribbons and curls.

A wig was "dressed" with powder and perfume.

T (F) 10. Philadelphia established the first public library in America in 1698.

Charleston, South Carolina, established the first public library in 1698.

T (F) 11. A favorite American beverage after the Boston Tea Party was hot cocoa.

A favorite American beverage after the Boston Tea Party was coffee.

(T) F 12. Puritans wore bright clothing and enjoyed good music.

_____

T (F) 13. Women in the colonies married much later than women in Europe.

Women in the colonies married much earlier than women in Europe.

(T) F 14. A popular addition to colonial plantations was a roofed porch called a piazza.

_____

(T) F 15. The late seventeenth-century infant death rate in the colonies was significantly lower than in Europe.

_____

Crossword Puzzle

Complete the following crossword puzzle.

ACROSS

3. standard fare on frontier farm dinner tables
5. a three-legged, covered pot
6. toppings for well-dressed colonial men
9. a single page of a book sold for a penny
10. end of the Great Philadelphia Wagon Road
11. one common social event on the frontier
13. bondsman
16. one of the large groups of non-English settlers
18. a group from Germany, not the Netherlands
19. common name for village school
21. mixture of linen and wool
24. *Poor Richard's* author
25. South Carolina grain crop
26. urged smallpox inoculations

DOWN

1. cornbread made from meal and sour milk
2. Indian crop made popular worldwide
4. common home in the colonial backcountry
6. reigns at thirty years of age (*Poor Richard's*)
7. roofed porch on a southern home
8. Education should provide the ability to read this.
12. Poor Richard says, "Plow deep while sluggards __."
14. catches few flies (*Poor Richard's*)
15. A budget wig was called the __ *Buckle.*
17. "Williamsburg style" or "__ style"
20. paddle-shaped "book" made of this
22. time to go to bed and to rise (*Poor Richard's*)
23. "makes waste" (*Poor Richard's*)

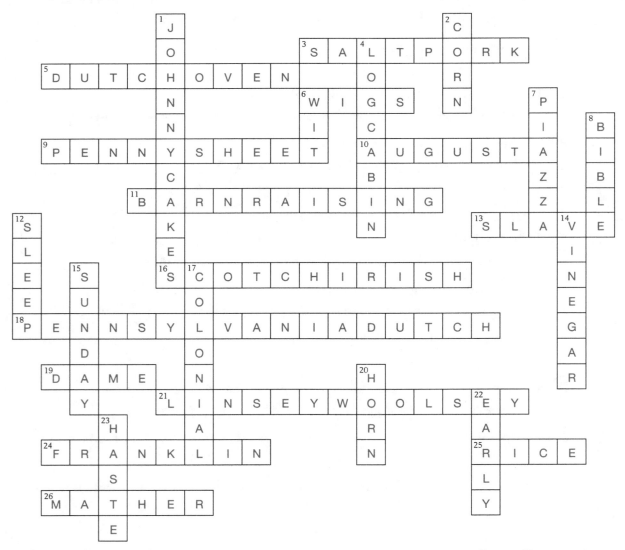

SKILL: Recognition

Map Study: Religion in the Colonies

Refer to the map on pages x and xi as well as to the text to complete the activity below.

1. Label the colonies with their correct names. Names that are too large may be put to the side with a line drawn to the colony being labeled.

2. Use the following symbols to show the major areas in which the following religious groups settled.

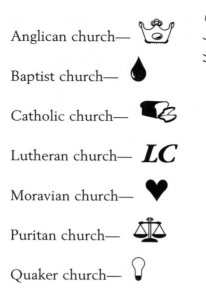

Anglican church—

Baptist church—

Catholic church—

Lutheran church— *LC*

Moravian church—

Puritan church—

Quaker church—

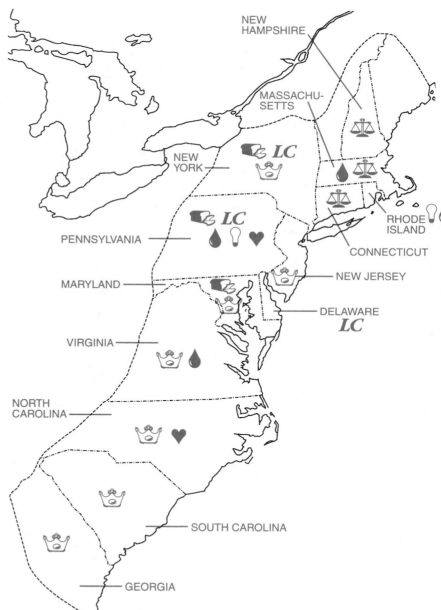

3. Which colony seems to have the greatest numbers of religions represented?

Pennsylvania

4. List the religions, mentioned in the text, that settled in that colony.

Baptist, Catholic, Lutheran,

Moravian, and Quaker

Early Denominations and Their Leaders

Match the denomination names with the phrase that best describes them.

___D___ 1. Puritan church that elected its own officers

___E___ 2. allowed unconverted members to have full privileges of citizenship

___M___ 3. guided by "Inner Light"; also called "Friends"

___K___ 4. emphasized conversion and holy living

___B___ 5. refused to serve in the military or to hold office

___J___ 6. followers of John Huss; conducted much mission work

___G___ 7. agreed with the Puritans but saw no problem in the Anglican church's ceremonies

___C___ 8. emphasized doctrine of baptism by immersion

___I___ 9. numerically the most important Anabaptists

___F___ 10. believed Anglican system of church government was divinely ordained

___H___ 11. followed teachings of Martin Luther

___L___ 12. church members voted on ruling elders, who voted on the next level of church authority, etc.

___A___ 13. more conservative Anabaptists; practiced strict church discipline

A. Amish
B. Anabaptists
C. Baptists
D. Congregationalists
E. Half-Way Covenant
F. high church Anglicans
G. low church Anglicans
H. Lutherans
I. Mennonites
J. Moravians
K. Pietists
L. Presbyterians
M. Quakers

Match the preacher with his denomination.

___F___ 14. George Fox

___C___ 15. Menno Simons

___A___ 16. Roger Williams

___E___ 17. Francis Makemie

___D___ 18. Count Zinzendorf

___B___ 19. Henry Mühlenberg

A. Baptist
B. Lutheran
C. Mennonite
D. Moravian
E. Presbyterian
F. Quaker

Colonial Sunday

Put words in the blanks that will correctly complete the paragraph.

I just heard the (1) ____drums or bell____ from the church, and mother and father are urging us out the door. It is so cold this November morning! As we enter the church, I look longingly at the (2) ____box____ ____pew____ that the Hancock family bought. Oh, to be away from the drafts that swirl around inside the room. Our church was built just last summer; so it is very modern. Our pastor preaches from a (3) ____wine____ ____glass____ pulpit. He looks so majestic! The new (4) ____sounding____ ____board____ helps his voice carry to every corner of the church as he prays through the (5) ____bills____ ____of____ ____request____. Morning service goes quickly, and it is time for (6) ____catechism____ class. My sister and I have practiced, and we know all the correct responses. After lunch we come back to afternoon services. I love to sing the psalms from the (7) ____Bay____ ____Psalm____ ____Book____. My favorite is the (8) "____Old____ ____Hundredth____" based on Psalm 100. I look toward the (9) ____balcony____ where the Hancocks' (10) ____servants____ sit. They had to get up there by a (11) ____ladder____ on the outside of the church. When we sing, their voices sound like those of angels drifting down, mixing with the congregational voices as the (12) ____precentor____ (13) "____lines____ ____out____" a hymn. The service grows long, and

I flinch as the pastor flips over the (14) ____hourglass____ and continues reading his sermon. Poor Mr. Anders in the pew in front is falling asleep. Oh, oh! Here comes the (15) ____usher____ to give him a rap on the head. Seeing that, I know I will be wide awake the rest of the service.

What Is Missing?

Fill in the blanks with the correct answer.

1. A school founded to train Indians but eventually opened to whites was _____Dartmouth_____ College.

2. The first Bible printed in America was in the _____Algonquin_____ Indian language.

3. The Swedish Lutheran John _____Campanius_____ worked among the Delaware Indians.

4. Roger _____Williams_____ was one of the first white men in New England to preach to the Indians.

5. John Eliot's converts formed communities called _____praying_____ villages.

6. Many congregationalists sadly mistook _____civilization_____ for salvation and forced European standards on the Indians.

7. Although David Brainerd died young, his _____Journal_____ inspired many young men to enter mission work.

8. One of the most successful Moravian missions, "Gnadenhutten," was directed by David _____Zeisberger_____.

9. Congregationalists and Moravians did extensive work in Indian_____missions_____.

10. _____Jonathan_____ _____Edwards_____ entered Yale before he was fourteen and was perhaps the greatest theologian of the Great Awakening.

11. The Great Awakening affected _____social_____ and _____political_____ life as well as religious.

12. _____George_____ _____Whitefield_____ was the Great Awakening's outstanding evangelist.

13. In New England the _____Half-Way_____ _____Covenant_____ was slowly filling Congregational churches with unconverted members.

14. The Awakening was a breakthrough for _____personal_____ _____liberty_____ because it reaffirmed the _____equality_____ of _____all_____ _____men_____ before God.

15. The Great Awakening was a powerful _____social_____, _____political_____, and _____religious_____ force that permanently altered the face of _____American_____ _____history_____.

French and Indian Questions

Write the answers to the questions in the blanks provided.

1. What Ottawa Indian chief led a war against the British after the French and Indian War? _Pontiac_

2. What treaty brought an end to Queen Anne's War?
   Treaty of Utrecht

3. What general tried to capture Fort Duquesne by organized, open battle?
   Edward Braddock

4. What is a method of warfare that uses sudden surprise attacks by small groups of hidden troops? _guerrilla_

5. What was Ben Franklin's plan to centralize the colonial rule?
   Albany Congress

6. What treaty removed French influence as a major force in North America?
   Treaty of Paris

7. What French Canadian leader caused great trouble for the English settlements in King William's War? _Frontenac_

8. What group did the British forcibly remove from Nova Scotia?
   Acadians

9. Which talented soldier and engineer of defeats against the British was given command of French forces in America? _Montcalm_

10. In which battle near Quebec did the British rout the French, bringing an end to the war? _Battle of the Plains of Abraham_

11. Which prime minister of Great Britain developed a plan to win the war?
    William Pitt

12. Where did a large force of French soldiers and Indian warriors wait for Washington and his men? _Fort Duquesne_

13. Which British commander was given the key campaign of the war?
    James Wolfe

14. What powerful fortress in North America controlled the mouth of the St. Lawrence River? _Louisbourg_

15. What was the key campaign of the war?
    French Canadian capital, Quebec

Map Study: French and Indian Wars

Use the maps on pages 89, 94, and 95 of the text and an atlas to complete this map study. Some locations may need to be approximated.

1. Label the following. Cities will be shown with dots; forts will be shown with solid triangles.

Lakes—Erie, Ontario, and Champlain

Rivers—Hudson, St. Lawrence, Mississippi, and Ohio

Places—Albany, Boston, Montreal, New Orleans, Quebec, Nova Scotia

Forts—Fort Detroit, Fort Duquesne, Fort Frontenac, Fort Michilimackinac, Fort Niagara, Fort William Henry

2. Color the following:

Yellow—First location of the Acadians

Red—Relocation site for many Acadians

Black line—Around French holdings before Treaty of Paris

Blue—Spanish portion of former French holdings

Green—British portion of former French holdings

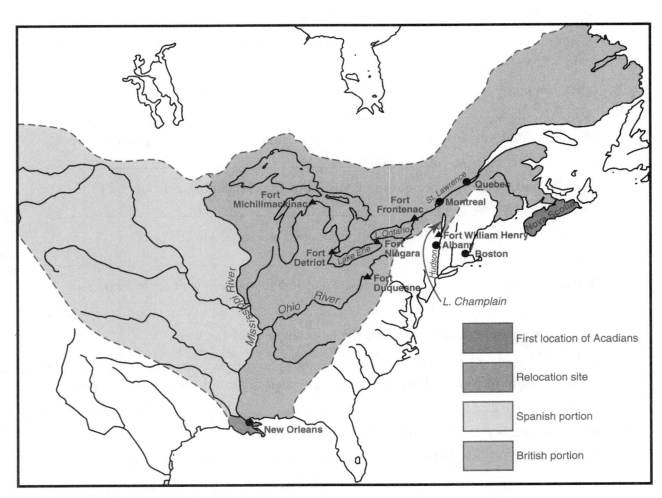

Ordering

Put the following lists in chronological order.

French and Indian War	1.	King William's War
King George's War	2.	Queen Anne's War
King William's War	3.	Treaty of Utrecht
Pontiac's War	4.	King George's War
Queen Anne's War	5.	French and Indian War
Treaty of Paris	6.	Treaty of Paris
Treaty of Utrecht	7.	Pontiac's War
Proclamation Line	8.	Proclamation Line
Quartering Act	9.	Sugar Act
Townshend Acts	10.	Stamp Act
Stamp Act	11.	Quartering Act
Sugar Act	12.	Townshend Acts

Describe the five parliamentary decisions above and tell how they affected the colonists.

13. The Proclamation Line forbade colonists to settle beyond the Appalachian Mountains. For the most part, colonists ignored the decree and continued to expand westward. The cities of Pittsburgh and Wheeling were begun during the time after the line was drawn.

14. The Sugar Act put a tariff on imported goods such as sugar, molasses, and coffee supposedly to defray "the expenses of defending, protecting, and securing" the colonies. Because of British occupation, the colonists felt that their legislatures had been rendered virtually powerless.

15. The Stamp Act levied the first "internal" tax. It taxed items such as legal and commercial documents and newspapers produced and used in the colonies only. Once again the colonists felt that their legislatures were being overridden.

16. The Quartering Act said that the colonists must submit to a British army during times of peace and provide them with food and other necessary supplies. The colonists felt that they were being occupied by the military to enforce the taxation.

17. The Townshend Acts proposed taxes on glass, paint, paper, and tea. They also strengthened writs of assistance and search warrants used by officials to look for taxable items. The tax monies were to be used to pay salaries of royal officials, thus taking "power of the purse" away from the colonists.

Crossword Puzzle

Across

1. fort at the Forks of the Ohio
6. a French padre who paddled far down the Mississippi
9. French territory later given to Spain
14. queen after whom a war was named
16. led French Canadians during King William's War
18. site of the battle for Quebec
20. British prime minister with a plan
21. cut a road for his troops but was killed in the battle
22. tax on goods produced and consumed in the colonies
23. British minister intent on balancing the books
24. claimed Louisiana for France
25. site of a congress promoting colonial unity
26. half of a French explorer duo

Down

2. French Canadian capital
3. taxed along with molasses and coffee
4. took Louisbourg and Quebec for the British
5. Virginia colonel who surrendered Fort Necessity
6. French commander in French and Indian War
7. law subjecting colonies to a standing army in peace
8. important power to be held by colonial assemblies
10. "first blood" of the Revolution
11. His "Acts" brought angry reactions.
12. "the War" that ended in 1763
13. the "Farmer in Pennsylvania"
15. forbade settlement beyond Appalachians
17. declared, "Give me liberty, or give me death!"
18. 1763 treaty that changed the face of North America
19. proposed the Albany Plan

Across solution entries: 1 DUQUESNE, 6 MARQUETTE, 9 LOUISIANA, 14 ANNE, 16 COMTEDEFRONTENAC, 18 PLAINSOFABRAHAM, 20 PITT, 21 BRADDOCK, 22 INTERNAL, 23 GRENVILLE, 24 LASALLE, 25 ALBANY, 26 JOLIET

Down solution entries: 2 QUEBEC, 3 SUGAR, 4 WOLFE, 5 WASHINGTON, 6 MONTCALM, 7 QUARTERING, 8 PURSE, 10 BOSTONMASSACRE, 11 TOWNSHEND, 12 FRENCHANDINDIAN, 13 DICKINSON, 15 PROCLAMATION, 17 HENRY, 18 PARIS, 19 FRANKLIN

Explosive Events

Fill in the bursts with the events that are recorded on pages 106-9 of the text.

American Action	*British Action*

1.
Gaspee burned

British court of inquiry established—
"purse strings" taken

2.
Tea Act of 1773

Committee of Correspondence
formed

3.
Boston Tea Party

Coercive Acts & Quebec Act

4.
Gage confiscates
Patriot gunpowder.

Continental Congress

5.
Declaration of
American Rights

Gage goes to Concord to seize muni-
tions stockpile.

6.
Battles of Lexington and
Concord

Conflict Conclusions

Evaluate the following events and battles covered on pages 115-22 of the text. Tell whether each one helped or hurt the American cause by checking the appropriate box, and then defend your viewpoint in the blanks provided.

┌─**Helped**
│ ┌─**Hurt**

Students' answers will vary.

☐ ☑ 1. Battle of Long Island The battle hurt the American cause in that an important city was lost. It also revealed to the British the American military incompetence. It may have helped in that it showed the Americans how much work they had to do to get their troops ready for continued battle.

☑ ☐ 2. Sea battle of the *Bonhomme Richard* and *Serapis* The Americans had such a small navy that victory at sea was not expected. Their victory helped to stir up confidence and "to set a tradition of victory" for the United States Navy.

☑ ☐ 3. Attack on Trenton The Americans needed a victory in the army to encourage re-enlistment, and the attack on Trenton was one such victory. The victory in Trenton was overwhelming, and it bolstered the Americans' confidence to continue through the winter.

☐ ☑ 4. Battle of Brandywine When this battle was lost, so was the capital city, and the Continental army was embarrassed. The loss hurt America because it forced a retreat.

☑ ☐ 5. Battle of Monmouth Although the battle was a draw, it did help the Americans show the British their new professionalism and helped to confirm the British decision to move their campaign to the South.

Map Study: The Revolution

Refer to the text, the maps on pages 111, 118, 123, and 124 of the text, and an atlas to complete this study.

1. Label the following locations. Battle locations are marked with a star; forts are marked with a solid triangle; and other locations are marked with a dot. Trace the rivers with blue colored pencil and label them.

Augusta	Bennington	Brandywine	Bunker Hill
Camden	Charleston	Concord	Cowpens
Delaware River	Fort Moultrie	Fort Ticonderoga	Guilford Court House
Hudson River	Kings Mountain	Lake Champlain	Lexington
Long Island	Monmouth	New York City	Philadelphia
Princeton	Saratoga	Trenton	Valley Forge
West Point	Wilmington, N.C.	Yorktown	

2. Complete the following chart dealing with the major battles. (Use *B* for British and *A* for American.)

Battle	Date	Who won	Colony	Commanders B/A
Bunker Hill	June 16, 1775	B	Massachusetts	Gage/unnamed
Princeton	Jan. 3, 1777	A	New Jersey	Cornwallis/Washington
Saratoga	Sept.-Oct. 1777	A	New York	Burgoyne/Gates, Morgan, Arnold
Kings Mountain	Oct. 7, 1780	A	South Carolina	Ferguson/Shelby, Sevier
Camden	Aug. 16, 1780	B	South Carolina	Cornwallis/Gates
Cowpens	Jan. 1, 1781	A	South Carolina	Tarleton/Morgan

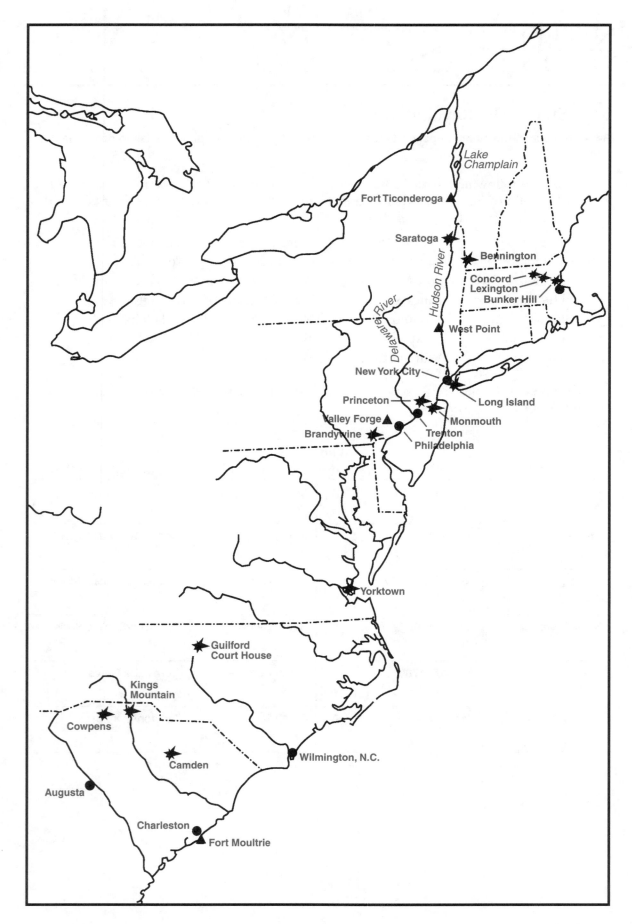

Lake Champlain

Fort Ticonderoga ▲

Saratoga ★

★ Bennington

Concord
Lexington
Bunker Hill

Hudson River

Delaware River

West Point ▲

New York City

Princeton

Valley Forge ▲

Brandywine ★

Monmouth

Trenton
Philadelphia

Long Island

Yorktown

Guilford
Court House ★

Kings
Mountain

Cowpens ★

Camden ★

Wilmington, N.C.

Augusta

Charleston

Fort Moultrie ▲

Military Melee

Put the correct letter in the blank provided.

_____I_____ 1. Cornwallis's Waterloo

_____D_____ 2. captured Vincennes with a force of 150 men

_____Q_____ 3. the author of *Common Sense*

_____F_____ 4. forced the British to evacuate Boston

_____P_____ 5. the main author of the Declaration of Independence

_____N_____ 6. professional soldiers

_____K_____ 7. Molly Pitcher became a legend in this battle.

_____H_____ 8. British general who surrendered Fort Ticonderoga

_____C_____ 9. commanded the "Green Mountain Boys"

_____J_____ 10. citizen soldiers

_____G_____ 11. British-paid German soldiers

_____E_____ 12. whom Tarleton said "the devil himself could not catch"

_____T_____ 13. won the Battle of Long Island

_____M_____ 14. Americans who fought for independence

_____A_____ 15. German drillmaster for the Continental army

_____L_____ 16. document that pledged loyalty to the king

_____R_____ 17. Loyalists

_____O_____ 18. the turning point of the war

_____B_____ 19. brilliant soldier turned traitor

_____S_____ 20. Washington's famous crossing of the Delaware was to get to this.

A. Baron von Steuben
B. Benedict Arnold
C. Ethan Allen
D. George Rogers Clark
E. Francis Marion
F. Henry Knox
G. Hessians
H. John Burgoyne
I. Yorktown
J. militia
K. Monmouth
L. Olive Branch Petition
M. Patriots
N. regulars
O. Saratoga campaign
P. Thomas Jefferson
Q. Thomas Paine
R. Tories
S. Trenton
T. William Howe

Treaty of Paris, 1783

Summarize the following articles agreed to by the United States and Great Britain in the Treaty of Paris, 1783. Activity could be used in a class discussion.

Article 1: His Brittanic Majesty acknowledges the said United States, viz., New Hampshire, Massachusetts Bay, Rhode Island and Providence Plantations, Connecticut, New York, New Jersey, Pennsylvania, Maryland, Virginia, North Carolina, South Carolina and Georgia, to be free sovereign and independent states, that he treats with them as such, and for himself, his heirs, and successors relinquishes all claims to the government, property, and territorial rights of the same and every part thereof.

Colonies to be free, sovereign, and independent states. The king, his heirs, and successors give up all

claims to government, property, and territorial rights.

_____

Article 4: It is agreed that creditors on either side shall meet with no lawful impediment to the recovery of the full value in sterling money of all bona fide debts heretofore contracted.

Debts on both sides to be paid in British money in silver or gold.

_____

_____

Article 8: The navigation of the river Mississippi, from its source to the ocean, shall forever remain free and open to the subjects of Great Britain and the citizens of the United States.

U.S. citizens and British subjects have the right to freely use the Mississippi River from its source to

the ocean.

_____

Article 10: The solemn ratifications of the present treaty expedited in good and due form shall be exchanged between the contracting parties in the space of six months or sooner, if possible, to be computed from the day of the signatures of the present treaty. In witness whereof we the undersigned, their ministers plenipotentiary, have in their name and in virtue of our full powers, signed with our hands the present definitive treaty and caused the seals of our arms to be affixed thereto.

The terms of the treaty were to be fulfilled beginning the day the treaty was signed and to be completed

in six months or sooner.

_____

Map Study: Northwest Territory

Refer to the maps on pages x-xi, 136, and 138 and to the Appendix on page 658.

1. Label the following boundaries of the Northwest Territory:

   The Great Lakes—Erie, Huron, Ontario, Michigan, and Superior
   The Mississippi and Ohio Rivers

2. Label the thirteen original states and the dates of their entrance into the Union.

3. Highlight in green the boundary of the Northwest Territory and color the territory itself yellow.

4. Label in black the states that would later be formed in the territory and the dates of their entrance into the Union.

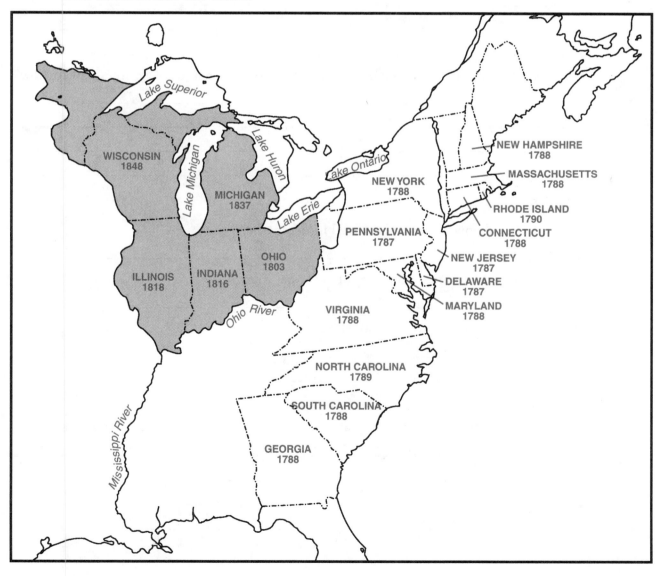

Separate Powers

Find two news articles that illustrate how any one of the three branches of government is currently exercising its powers. Answer the following questions about each article. If the article refers to two branches of government, you should choose one branch. Students' answers will vary.

ARTICLE I

1. What branch of government is involved in the article?

_____

2. What is the constitutional power granted to that branch?

_____

3. How does it exercise its constitutional power?

_____

_____

_____

4. Does its action result in a check or balance on another branch of government? If so, how?

_____

_____

_____

_____

ARTICLE II

1. What branch of government is involved in the article?

_____

2. What is the constitutional power granted to that branch?

_____

3. How does it exercise its constitutional power?

_____

_____

_____

4. Does its action result in a check or balance on another branch of government? If so, how?

_____

_____

_____

_____

SKILL: Synthesis

Who Am I?

Read each statement and decide who would have said it. Write the correct answer in the blank.

Daniel Shays	1. I was a Massachusetts farmer who tried to close the courts in the western part of the state.
Thomas Jefferson	2. I had a plan for dividing the Northwest Territory into ten states with names like "Cherronesus."
Alexander Hamilton	3. I wrote under the pen name "Publius."
Patrick Henry	4. I led the Anti-Federalists of Virginia with my fiery oratory.
George Washington	5. I read a letter and stopped a conspiracy.
James Madison	6. I was called the "Father of the Constitution."
George Clinton	7. I used the pen name "Cato" to denounce the Constitution.
John Adams	8. I was the first vice president of the United States.
Benjamin Franklin	9. I had often wondered whether it was a rising or a setting sun painted behind the president's chair; I was happy to know it was a rising sun.
Roger Sherman	10. My compromise saved the Constitutional Convention and the Constitution.
George Mason	11. Because it failed to guarantee civil liberties, I said that I "would sooner chop off [my] right hand" than sign the final draft of the Constitution.
John Dickinson	12. I headed the committee that wrote the Articles of Confederation.
John Hancock	13. As president of the Congress in 1776, I was the first person to sign the Declaration of Independence.
Daniel Webster	14. I said that I doubted "whether one single law of any lawgiver, ancient or modern, has produced effects of more distinct, marked, and lasting character than the ordinance of '87."

What's the Question?

Just what you've wanted, an assignment with all the answers. Now write questions to fit.

1. a close alliance of states _What is a confederation?_

2. changes or additions (to the Constitution) _What are amendments?_

3. having one house (congress) _What is a unicameral congress?_

4. having two houses (congress) _What is a bicameral congress?_

5. The new lands were divided into townships of thirty-six sections or lots of one square mile. _How was the Northwest Territory divided?_

6. May 25, 1787 _What was the date of the opening session of the Constitutional Convention?_

7. This plan wanted two houses with representation based on state population. _What was the Virginia Plan?_

8. This plan wanted one house with each state having one vote. _What was the New Jersey Plan?_

9. the Great Compromise, or Connecticut Compromise _What was the compromise that saved the Convention and the Constitution?_

10. They wanted their back pay, and some wanted to establish a new government under a king. _What did conspirators in the Newburgh Conspiracy want?_

11. United States government paper money _What are "continental dollars"?_

12. limited government _What was the underlying theme of the Constitution?_

13. the Three-Fifths Compromise _What was the numerical compromise that resolved the slavery issue?_

14. the electoral college _What is the indirect means used to elect the president?_

15. April 30, 1789 _On what date was George Washington inaugurated?_

16. "Rogue Island" _What was another name for the last state to ratify the Constitution?_

17. federalism _What is the division of power between national and state levels of government?_

18. gold or silver used as money _What is hard money?_

19. checks and balances _What principle balances the power of the three branches of government?_

20. popular sovereignty _What idea says that governmental power is of the people?_

Cabinet Confusion

Compare the growth of government by listing the offices in both Washington's cabinet and today's cabinet. Write the dates that today's cabinet positions were first established. Use your book and an almanac.

Washington's Cabinet

_____ Dept. of State

_____ Dept. of Treasury

_____ Dept. of War

Today's Cabinet   Date Established

Today's Cabinet	Date Established
Dept. of State	1789
Dept. of Treasury	1789
Dept. of Defense (originally the War Dept.)	1947
Dept. of Justice (Attorney General)	1870
Dept. of the Interior	1849
Dept. of Agriculture	1862
Dept. of Labor	1913
Dept. of Commerce	1913
Dept. of Housing and Urban Development	1965
Dept. of Transportation	1966
Dept. of Energy	1977
Dept. of Health and Human Services	1979
Dept. of Education	1979
Dept. of Veterans Affairs	1988

1. What does the number of departments in the cabinet say about the power of the federal government today? It shows that the power of the federal government has expanded into several more areas than the founders originally intended.

2. Why do you think so many departments were formed or split in the past twenty-two years? Answers may vary. Most of the departments have been formed or split to accommodate the growing population and urbanization.

The Second President of the United States

Use the textbook to finish the narrative.

My name is (1) _____John_____ _____Adams_____, and I am the second president of the United States. Much of what has affected my term of office took place during Washington's second term. In 1793, the British began attacking our ships. We thought that (2) _____Jay's_____ _____Treaty_____ would solve the problem, but it only caused (3) _____France_____ to become more hostile. They began raiding so many of our ships that we became embroiled in what was called a (4) _____Quasi_____ _____War_____; not formally declared war, but a conflict nonetheless. The French thought that we were so desperate for it to end that they sent agents to demand money from us to stop their raids. We refused, of course. Later, when Congress asked to see the correspondence regarding the affair, I dared not use the agents' real names; so it became known as the (5) _____XYZ_____ _____Affair_____. When the opportunity came to make peace, my political party, the (6) _____Federalists_____, were against me. To preserve my country meant losing their support. When the conflict ended with an anti-French sentiment in the colonies, it was easy for the Federalist Congress to propose the series of acts called the (7) _____Alien_____ and _____Sedition_____ Acts. The first act placed restrictions on immigrants and gave me much more power to imprison undesirables. The second act went too far, however, when it made it illegal to speak or write certain things against the government or the president. My opponents Jefferson and Madison were quick to respond with their (8) _____Kentucky_____ and _____Virginia_____ Resolutions respectively. Urging his supporters to make their views known by the ballot, (9) _____Jefferson_____ made his bid for the presidency well known. The decisions I made in office I made for my countrymen, but in doing so I lost their support. Even as the inauguration of the third president of the United States takes place today, I leave office knowing that my (10) _____"midnight_____ _____appointments"_____ will at least keep the Federalists in power in the judiciary.

False Impressions

Correctly identify the statement as true or false by circling the appropriate letter. If the statement is false, correct it to make it true.

T (F) 1. The first ten amendments to the Constitution were called the Judiciary Act of 1789.

<u>The first ten amendments to the Constitution were called the Bill of Rights.</u>

(T) F 2. In an effort to quiet political opposition, the Federalist-controlled Congress passed the Alien and Sedition Acts.

_____

T (F) 3. President Adams had "midnight appointments" with congressmen to try to influence their decisions.

<u>Adams made "midnight appointments" of judges the night before leaving office.</u>

T (F) 4. Adams and Jefferson remained bitter enemies till their deaths.

<u>Adams and Jefferson became good friends after their retirements.</u>

(T) F 5. Because of taxation on liquor production, backcountry Pennsylvania farmers rose up in what was called the Whiskey Rebellion.

_____

(T) F 6. Citizen Genêt tried to stir up pro-French feelings to persuade America to side with France against Britain.

_____

T (F) 7. The Jay Treaty achieved one great result; it averted war with France.

<u>The Jay Treaty achieved one great result; it averted war with Britain.</u>

(T) F 8. Washington appointed four men as an advisory group that later became known as the cabinet.

_____

T (F) 9. Thomas Jefferson proposed a bill and later persuaded Washington to sign it, creating the first National Bank.

<u>Alexander Hamilton proposed a bill and later persuaded Washington to sign it. . . .</u>

(T) F 10. Congress members who wanted more flexibility interpreting the Constitution on certain issues were called loose constructionists.

_____

(T) F 11. Hamilton's *Report on Public Credit* caused a stir that ended with the present site of the capital of the United States being chosen.

_____

T (F) 12. President Washington issued a Proclamation of Neutrality to avoid involvement in the clashes between Canada and Britain.

<u>The Proclamation of Neutrality tried to avoid involvement . . . between France and Britain.</u>

Early Political Parties

As the early political parties emerged, they had some sharp differences. Draw an *X* in the column of the party to which the center phrase or word applies and briefly explain how it applies.

FEDERALIST		*REPUBLICAN*
	Jefferson and Burr	X—Winners of the 1800 election
X—The Federalists believed that the propertied, monied class would provide a stable government. This class was usually made up of industrial and commercial leaders.	Future lay in commerce	
	Jeffersonians	X—Label given to the Republican party
X—This was the Federalist claim.	True keepers of the Constitution	
	Pro-French trade	X—Many were pro-French when they saw France's desire for independence. Sentiment changed as revolution became bloodthirsty.
X—The Federalist nominees for the 1800 election. They lost.	Adams and Pinckney	
X—Republican name for the Federalists	Hamiltonians	
	Future lay in farms	X—Republicans distrusted centralized government. They felt that the key to America's future was in its people and its land.
	Last line of defense against tyranny	X—The Republican claim during the 1790s
X—During the war between France and Britain, Federalists felt that the United States should support Britain because of that country's power and trade.	Pro-British trade	
X—Republican name for the Federalists	Monarchists	

SKILL: Charts

Explore It Further

Your text gives a brief account of the Lewis and Clark expedition. Use biographies or encyclopedias to answer the following questions and to fill out the map on the next page. Answers will vary in completeness depending on the sources used.

1. What president of the United States commissioned the expedition? __Thomas Jefferson__

2. What was the full name of the man who was in charge of the Lewis and Clark expedition? __Meriwether Lewis__

3. What was the full name of his fellow explorer? __William Rogers Clark__

4. What was their difference in rank? __Lewis was a captain. Clark was a lieutenant.__

5. When and from where did they embark on their journey? __May 14, 1804—St. Louis, Missouri__

6. What was the name of the slave that accompanied Clark? __York__

7. When and where did the one and only fatality of the expedition occur? __on Aug. 20, 1804, at Sioux City, Iowa__

8. Who died and how? __Sergeant Charles Floyd, probably of a ruptured appendix__

9. Who were the first hostile Indians encountered? __the Teton Sioux__

10. Where were they confronted? __Bad River, South Dakota__

11. What new animal did the expeditioners discover that they first described as a "barking squirrel"? __a prairie dog__

12. What especially ferocious animal did the explorers encounter? __the grizzly bear__

13. Lewis took a pet on the expedition with him. Its name was Shannon.
    What was it? __a dog__ What breed? __a Newfoundland__

14. Where did the explorers spend their first winter? __near present-day Bismarck, North Dakota__

15. What Indian tribe did they name their fort after? __the Mandan Indians__

16. What was the name of the Indian woman who went with the expedition? __Sacajawea__

17. What tribe was she from? __the Shoshone Indians__

18. In what present-day state did they find the waterfalls that they encountered on the Missouri River? __Montana__ What are they called? __the Great Falls__

19. Where did the explorers cross the continental divide? __Lemhi Pass in Idaho__

20. What river did Lewis name after his cousin Maria? __the Marias River in Montana__

21. When did they sight the Pacific Ocean? __November 7, 1805__

22. What was the name of the camp in Oregon they established to winter in? __Fort Clatsop__

23. Why was Captain Lewis shot? __He was mistaken for a deer.__

24. On the return home, the party divided for a while to explore different routes. Which way did Lewis's division go? __north to explore the Marias River__

25. Which way did Clark's half go? __south to explore the Yellowstone River__

26. On what date did they arrive back in St. Louis? __September 23, 1806__

Map Study: Lewis and Clark Expedition

Complete the map using the sources that you used to answer the questions on the previous page.

1. Label the following places. The states named were not yet established.

   Rivers—Bad River, Columbia River, Marias River, Mississippi River, Missouri River, Snake River, Yellowstone River

   States—Idaho, Iowa, Kansas, Missouri, Montana, Nebraska, North and South Dakota, Oregon, Washington, Wyoming

   Cities—Bismarck, North Dakota; St. Louis, Missouri; Sioux City, Iowa

   Places—Cascade Range, Bitterroot Mountains, Pacific Ocean, Rocky Mountains

2. Place the proper symbols on the map to show the landmarks listed below.

   Fort Mandan—light flag   Great Falls—drop of water

   Sgt. Floyd's grave—cross   Lolo Pass—dark star

   Lemhi Pass—light star   Fort Clatsop—dark flag

   Teton Sioux meeting—tomahawk

3. Draw with a black marker the route west that the expedition took.

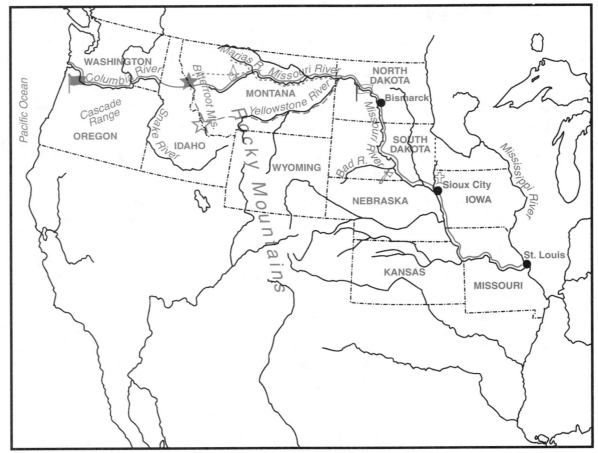

Questions and Profiles

Complete the following.

A. Answer the following questions.

1. Which Revolutionary hero did Washington appoint to crush early Indian uprisings?

   Mad Anthony Wayne

2. Which Indian claimed to have received a revelation from the "Master of Life"?

   Prophet

3. In which battle did the Indians think that the white man's weapons were charmed and, therefore, could not harm them? Tippecanoe

4. What was the trouble with treaties between the Americans and the Indians?

   Americans did not always honor the treaties, and Indians did not understand them.

5. Which battle got its name because the fighting took place among trees knocked down by a storm? Battle of Fallen Timbers

6. Which natural event was used by an influential Indian to support his claims of supernatural power? eclipse

7. Which treaty opened the southern half of Ohio to settlers? Greenville

8. In the Battle of the Thames, which general routed British and Indian forces?

   William Henry Harrison

9. Which great Indian leader dreamed of an Indian confederation whose power could withstand the threat of the white man's takeover? Tecumseh

B. Write a brief profile of the following using information from the textbook.

1. Harrison— Son of a Virginia governor and signer of the Declaration of Independence, joined the army and was an aide to Wayne at Fallen Timbers, entered politics and served as governor of Indiana Territory, believed Indians should receive full help and protection from government, insisted Indians give up their traditional way of life

2. Tecumseh— Great Indian leader in North America, part of Shawnee tribe, raised as a warrior, tried to get Indian tribes to form a single confederation, persuasive in speech, was fearless and had a code of honor that prevented torturing prisoners or attacking women and children

Map Study: The War of 1812

To complete this activity, refer to the map on page 185 of the text.

1. Label the new states that had joined the Union by 1812. Below each name, write the year in which the state was accepted into the Union. Refer to the Appendix on page 658.

   Vermont, Kentucky, Tennessee, Ohio, Louisiana

2. Label with a triangle Fort Dearborn, Fort McHenry, and Fort Niagara.

3. Label the five Great Lakes.

4. Label with a star the following War of 1812 battle locations.

   Bladensburg; Lake Erie; the Thames; York; Lake Champlain; Washington, D.C.; New Orleans; Horseshoe Bend

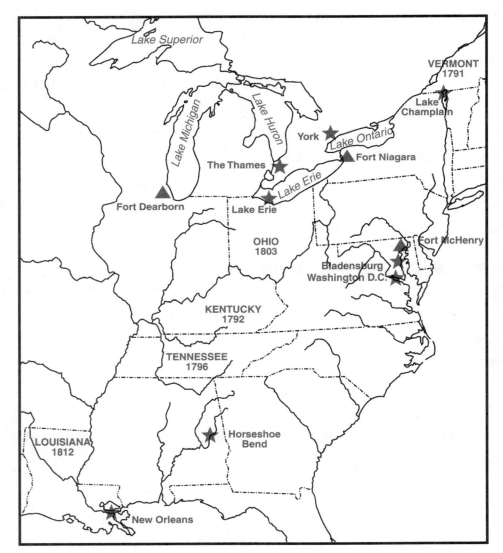

SKILL: Maps

The
Capitol Gazette
War of 1812 Prospectus

Intimations of War

In looking back, it seems that the British were bent on generating hostilities with the United States. Their total disregard for the citizenship of our people was displayed in the random (1) _____impressment_____ of our seamen into British service. Of course, the (2) _____Chesapeake_____ affair almost brought about the war in 1807. The American people were incensed that the captain of the British ship (3) _____Leopard_____ would kill and take Americans. If it weren't for the fact that (4) _____Jefferson_____ persuaded Congress to ban all trade with the rest of the world in the (5) _____Embargo Act_____, we would have gone to war immediately.

Flying Toward Conflict

Congress soon found that those most hurt by the trade ban were not the British or French, but the (6) _____Americans_____. In the 1810 congressional elections, several prowar representatives joined the House. These intensely nationalistic men were called (7) _____War Hawks_____ and were headed by (8) _____Henry Clay_____ of Kentucky and (9) _____John C. Calhoun_____ of South Carolina. These men and their supporters began pressuring the United States president, (10) _____James Madison_____,

to declare war on England. On (11) _____June 1, 1812_____, the president sent a war message to Congress. After heated debate, war was declared.

On Land and at Sea

Little did the glorious British navy expect to have the upstart American navy win so many battles. One factor was the oak-sided American ship the (12) _____Constitution_____, nicknamed (13) _____"Old Ironsides"_____. British cannonballs bounced right off. Another factor was the determination of the American captain (14) _____Oliver Hazard Perry_____, who built his own ships, dragged cannons through the wilderness to Lake Erie, and used sailors who had never been on anything larger than a flatboat. The British met defeat at his hands in the Battle of (15) _____Lake Erie_____. In spite of victories in the Northwest Territory, the outlook was gloomy for the U.S. when Napoleon surrendered and England could turn all its attention to America. Against Tennessee general (16) _____Andrew Jackson_____, the British suffered devastating defeat. Meanwhile, the (17) _____Treaty of Ghent_____ was signed in England. With that, the war was ended—a peace without victory.

Headlines!

Write news articles for two of the following headlines. Remember to include the important facts: who, what, when, where, why, and how. You may want to do extra research.

Neutrality Impossible   "Old Ironsides" Victorious
War Hawks Gaining Ground   Attack on Fort McHenry Repulsed
Tecumseh's Forces Narrowly Defeated   "Old Hickory," the New Hero

TITLE: _____

The students should use good writing technique, making sure to include a topic sentence and good

support in each article. The students should also be creative and exciting in their reporting of the events.

The teacher should check the articles against the text for accuracy.

_____

_____

_____

_____

_____

_____

_____

_____

_____

_____

TITLE: _____

_____

_____

_____

_____

_____

_____

_____

_____

_____

_____

_____

_____

Map Study: The Missouri Compromise

Refer to page 196 of the text to complete this map.

1. With red pencil, draw and label the Missouri Compromise line (36° 30').

2. Label all the states that were in the Union by 1821.

3. At the bottom left of the map, make a color key to identify the following areas and then color those areas according to your key.

   Free states   Slave states
   Free territory   Slave territory

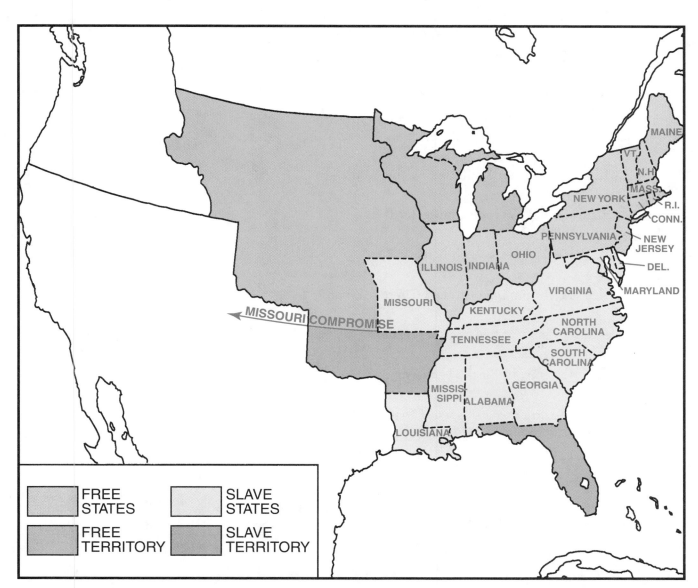

MAINE

VT.

N.H.

MASS.

NEW YORK

R.I.

CONN.

PENNSYLVANIA

NEW JERSEY

OHIO

DEL.

ILLINOIS INDIANA

VIRGINIA

MARYLAND

MISSOURI

KENTUCKY

MISSOURI COMPROMISE

NORTH CAROLINA

TENNESSEE

SOUTH CAROLINA

MISSIS SIPPI ALABAMA

GEORGIA

LOUISIANA

FREE STATES

SLAVE STATES

FREE TERRITORY

SLAVE TERRITORY

Time Travels

Put the letter for the correct date next to the event listed. Dates may be used more than once or not at all.

___O___ 1. Harrison's death

___F___ 2. Jackson's first election

___N___ 3. completion of the National Road

___E___ 4. last caucus nomination

___C___ 5. Missouri Compromise

___A___ 6. first protective tariff

___E___ 7. John Q. Adams's election

___F___ 8. first tariff nullified by the South

___I___ 9. Clay's Compromise Tariff

___H___ 10. Jackson's second election

___M___ 11. beginning of forced Cherokee march

___L___ 12. start of five-year depression

___H___ 13. start of Black Hawk War

___K___ 14. order to use "specie" for land

___J___ 15. beginning of the Seminole War

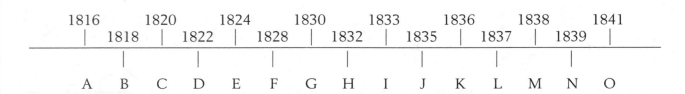

```
  1816        1820       1824       1830       1833       1836       1838       1841
     |    1818   |   1822  |   1828  |   1832  |   1835  |   1837  |   1839  |
  ___|_____|_____|_____|_____|_____|_____|_____|_____
        |         |         |         |         |         |         |         |
     A    B    C    D    E    F    G    H    I    J    K    L    M    N    O
```

Presidential Powers

Put the letter of the correct answer in the blank provided.

___B___ 1. closed meeting to select candidates

___A___ 2. accusation made against Adams and Clay

___F___ 3. clubs that supported Van Buren

___O___ 4. Cherokees' forced march to Oklahoma

___C___ 5. Jackson's real advisors

___R___ 6. Andrew Jackson

___M___ 7. higher protective import tax of 1828

___D___ 8. Martin Van Buren

___J___ 9. state institutions used for federal deposits

___P___ 10. caused by cotton price drop and irresponsible bank action

___N___ 11. campaign cry for Harrison and his running mate

___E___ 12. South Carolinian doctrine of rejecting unacceptable congressional acts as unconstitutional

___L___ 13. presidential practice of replacing government officials with supporters

___H___ 14. leader of Seminole Indians

___K___ 15. prohibition of the use of anything but hard money for land purchase

___I___ 16. economic collapse and five-year depression

___Q___ 17. the resolution which once again evened the political balance of slave and free states

___G___ 18. gave the president war powers against South Carolina

A. "corrupt bargain"
B. "King Caucus"
C. "Kitchen Cabinet"
D. "Little Magician"
E. nullification
F. "O.K."
G. Force Bill
H. Osceola
I. Panic of 1837
J. "pet banks"
K. Specie Circular of 1836
L. spoils system
M. "Tariff of Abominations"
N. "Tippecanoe and Tyler too"
O. Trail of Tears
P. Panic of 1819
Q. Missouri Compromise
R. "Old Hickory"

Crossword Puzzle

Across

1. Adams's wing of the Democratic-Republicans
3. Sauk and Fox leader who waged war
4. a challenging group against the two-party system
6. improvements promoted by the American system
7. great orator of the Senate who defended the Union
8. Old Hickory's close advisors in the White House
12. high tariff of 1828
13. an internal improvement ending in Vandalia, Illinois
16. the other state admitted by the Missouri Compromise
17. Jackson's party
20. a depression such as the one in 1819
21. South Carolina senator who spoke up for secession
22. scarred by a sabre and shot in a duel
23. Van Buren's replacement for pet banks
24. Osceola's Indians

Down

1. doctrine proposed by Calhoun
2. gathering of party delegates to nominate candidates
5. partisan replacement of officeholders
7. new anti-Jackson party
9. type of bargain allegedly made by Adams and Clay
10. tax on imported goods
11. type of banks in which Jackson placed federal deposits
14. Clay's economic nationalism; the "___ system"
15. a president, like his father
18. the "Little Magician"
19. closed nomination meeting of party leaders

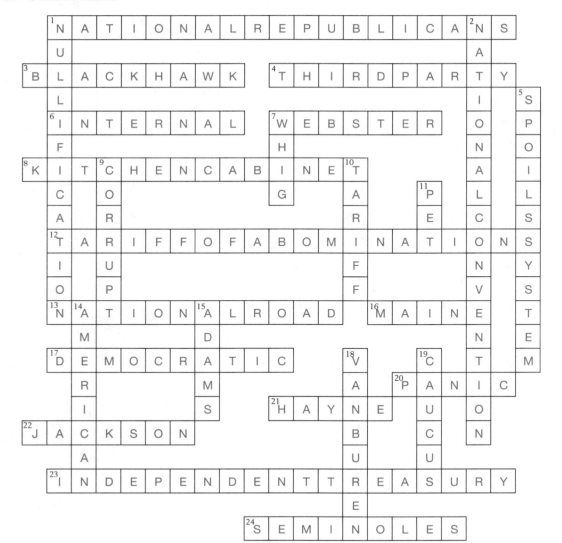

SKILL: Recognition

Map Study: The Growth of Transportation

Refer to page 221 of the text to complete this map.

1. Label the following places.

    Erie Canal, Chesapeake and Ohio Canal (C & O), Miami and Erie Canal (M & E), Ohio and Erie Canal, Wabash and Erie Canal, Lake Erie, Lake Michigan, Lake Ontario

2. Place a dot (•) with the city's name at the correct location for each of the following.

    Albany, Baltimore, Boonesboro, Buffalo, Cleveland, Evansville, Louisville, Natchez, New Orleans, Philadelphia, Richmond, Toledo, Vandalia

3. Draw and label the following: National Road, Natchez Trace, Wilderness Road.

Think About It!

It has been said, "Necessity is the mother of invention." Explain how the following inventions, transportation methods, and communication devices satisfied a need.

Invention		*Need*	*Previous Method*
Eli Whitney's interchangeable parts	1.	An easier method for replacing parts of machinery	Craftsmen handmade each part to fit each separate machine.
John Deere's steel-edged plow	2.	Way to plow through Northwest sod	Wooden plows and later iron plows
Eli Whitney's cotton gin	3.	Method for cleaning the seed from the cotton	Slaves had to hand-pick seeds from the cotton.
Robert Fulton's steamship	4.	A means for transporting goods upstream	Boats were pulled upstream, or goods went over land.
Governor Clinton's Erie Canal	5.	A more cost-effective way to transport goods	Goods were taken by horse along rivers and bad roads.
Samuel Morse's telegraph	6.	Faster communication across land and sea	Postal system in the East, pony express in the West

Optional Activity

Define a need (other than social or moral) in today's society and design an invention to satisfy that need.

SKILL: Evaluation

Who Am I?

Read each statement and decide whom or what it best describes in art, architecture, or literature.

<u>G. C. Bingham</u>	1. I was a "thorough democrat" who painted the common man.
<u>Benjamin West</u>	2. Although I spent most of my life in England, I greatly influenced and taught many American painters.
<u>Lowell Mason</u>	3. I published many popular hymnbooks.
<u>Edgar Allan Poe</u>	4. As the master short-story writer of America, I wrote of the dark, tortured depths of man's soul.
<u>Stephen Foster</u>	5. I dreamed of my wife, Jeanie, and wrote a ballad about my dream.
<u>Washington Irving</u>	6. I helped to develop the short story with works such as "Rip Van Winkle" and "The Legend of Sleepy Hollow."
<u>Charles Bullfinch and Benjamin Latrobe</u>	7. We used Greek revivalist architecture for the U.S. Capitol.
<u>Walt Whitman</u>	8. In *Leaves of Grass*, I celebrated the glory and nobility of man.
<u>Hudson River School</u>	9. As a group, we specialized in portraying the beauty and serenity of America.
<u>Gilbert Stuart</u>	10. I left a portrait unfinished, and it now appears on the one-dollar bill.
<u>Henry David Thoreau</u>	11. In *Walden*, I wrote about my stay on Walden Pond.
<u>James Fenimore Cooper</u>	12. I wrote romantic views of the American frontier.
<u>Federalist style</u>	13. This style of art duplicated the neoclassical style of Europe.

Reform and Religion

Using the textbook, fill in the following table.

Reform	Leader(s)	Changes Desired
Abolition	William Lloyd Garrison	Desired to eliminate slavery
Women's rights	(no central leader given in the book)	Desired equal rights and suffrage for women
Mental illness	Dorothea Dix	Desired to improve sanitary conditions and treatment of inmates of asylums
Education	Horace Mann William McGuffey	Desired public education and better teacher training; desired to include the gospel in public education
Prohibition	(no central leader given in the book)	Desired a ban on sales and consumption of alcohol
Utopian reform	George Rapp Robert Owen	Desired to establish perfect communities as models of social reform

Matching

__E__ 1. "New Measures"

__J__ 2. Mormonism

__H__ 3. "father of American Methodism"

__M__ 4. African Methodist Episcopal Church bishop

__I__ 5. originator of the camp meeting

__O__ 6. set a date for Christ's return

__K__ 7. supposed incarnation of God

__L__ 8. primary creator of transcendentalism

__N__ 9. preached messages that led to revival at Yale

__D__ 10. greatest camp meeting held

__A__ 11. first American mission board

__C__ 12. series of religious services lasting several days

__F__ 13. traveling from settlement to settlement in order to preach

__B__ 14. first great hero of American missions

__G__ 15. belief that God created the universe and then stood back and left it alone

A. ABCFM
B. Adoniram Judson
C. camp meeting
D. Cane Ridge, Kentucky
E. Charles Finney
F. circuit riding
G. deism
H. Francis Asbury
I. James McGready
J. Joseph Smith
K. Mother Ann Lee
L. Ralph Waldo Emerson
M. Richard Allen
N. Timothy Dwight
O. William Miller

Remember the Alamo!

Do some extra research in the library or with an encyclopedia at home. Look into the lives of three of the people listed below and answer the following questions about them.

Jim Bowie, Davy Crockett, Santa Anna, William Travis

Person 1 _____Jim Bowie / Davy Crockett_____

1. Where and when was he born? _Logan County, Kentucky, in 1796 / In eastern Tennessee on August 17, 1786_

2. Who was his wife? _____Marla Ursula de Vermendi / Mary (Polly) Finley, and later, Elizabeth Patton_

3. How did he happen to be at the Alamo? _He was commander of the Alamo. / He came in with the Texas_ volunteers.

4. How did he contribute to the battle? _Reports vary. One report says he was drunk much of the time in the_ last days, finally becoming so ill that he was bedridden until the end. / His group of volunteers came in February to prepare for the final assault on the Alamo.

5. What was the date of his death, and how old was he? _March 6, 1836 – 40 years old / March 6, 1836 –_ 50 years old

Person 2 _____Santa Anna / William Travis_____

1. Where and when was he born? _Jalapa, Mexico, on February 21, 1795(?) / Redbanks, S.C., on August 9, 1809_

2. Who was his wife? _He wasn't married. / He wasn't married._

3. How did he happen to be at the Alamo? _He led the Mexican Army against the Texans at the Alamo. / He_ brought a contingent of twenty-five men as reinforcements.

4. How did he contribute to the battle? _He led 6,000 Mexican soldiers against the Alamo to try to prevent_ Texas's independence efforts. His troops defeated the Americans at the Alamo. / Shortly after he arrived with reinforcements, he had to take command of the fort because of Bowie's illness.

5. What was the date of his death, and how old was he? _June 26, 1876 – approximately 81 years old /_ March 6, 1836 – 27 years old

Person 3 _____

1. Where and when was he born? _____

2. Who was his wife? _____

3. How did he happen to be at the Alamo? _____

_____

4. How did he contribute to the battle? _____

_____

_____

5. What was the date of his death, and how old was he? _____

_____

From Sea to Shining Sea

Use the text to fill in the table. Look back to previous chapters to find the information on Florida.

Territory	Prior Occupation	How Obtained	Date	New Boundaries
Texas	Mexico	Mexican/American War	1845	Rio Grande
Oregon	Britain/U.S.	treaty	1846	49th parallel
Maine	Britain/U.S.	Webster/Ashburton Treaty	1842	U.S. received 7/12 of disputed area
Florida	Spain	Adams/Onis Treaty	1821	Annexed entire peninsula

Page 242 of the text quotes these words of John Louis O'Sullivan:

> Our manifest destiny [is] to overspread and to possess the whole of the continent which Providence has given us for the development of the great experiment of liberty and federated self-government entrusted to us.

Do you think this statement is correct? Defend your position. Students' answers will vary.

Students who agree with the statement may agree on the basis that the cultures which were on the continent were not occupying all the land and were not bound under a single government and therefore did not have any claim to the land. They may also say that the cultures were so primitive that they actually benefited from the overspreading by the Americans. They may cite, as proof of this benefit, the numerous instances in which more powerful nations have overthrown and absorbed lesser nations and actually improved their technology, health, and economic structure.

Students who disagree with the statement may disagree on the basis that a culture's small size or primitive customs do not lessen its value. They may also question the boundaries described ("whole of the continent") since, according to the statement, the United States easily could have claimed Canada, Mexico, and Central America.

Mexican-American Relations

Put the letter for the correct date next to the event.

___N___ 1. Treaty of Guadalupe Hidalgo

___L___ 2. capture of Santa Fe

___A___ 3. first Texas settlement

___F___ 4. American troops first attacked by Mexican troops

___C___ 5. Battle of San Jacinto

___H___ 6. Bear Flag Republic established

___K___ 7. Scott's entrance into Vera Cruz

___E___ 8. Texas admitted to the Union

___J___ 9. Battle of Buena Vista

___G___ 10. declaration of war by Congress

___B___ 11. the battle at the Alamo

___M___ 12. Mexico City taken

___I___ 13. Taylor's assault on Monterrey

___D___ 14. election of President James K. Polk

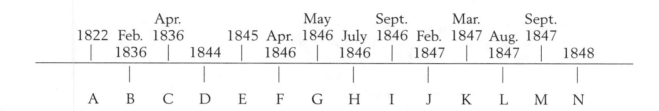

Treaty of Guadalupe Hidalgo, 1848

Summarize the following provisions agreed to by the United States and Mexico in the Treaty of Guadalupe Hidalgo. The activity may be used in a class discussion.

Article I: There shall be firm and universal peace between the United States of America and the Mexican Republic, and between their respective countries, territories, cities, towns, and people, without exception of places or persons.

Article I: There was to be total peace between the United States and Mexico in all areas, including people and territories.

Article XII: In consideration of the extension acquired by the boundaries of the United States, as defined in the fifth article of the present treaty, the Government of the United States engages to pay that of the Mexican Republic the sum of fifteen millions of dollars. . . .

Article XII: The United States was to pay the Mexican Republic 15 million dollars for territory gained.

Article XVI: Each of the contracting parties reserves to itself the entire right to fortify whatever point within its territory it may judge proper so to fortify for its security.

Article XVI: For protection, each country may set up fortifications within its boundaries in whatever way it chooses.

Article XXI: If unhappily any disagreement should hereafter arise between the Governments of the two republics, whether with respect to the interpretation of any stipulation in this treaty, or with respect to any other particular concerning the political or commercial relations of the two nations, the said Governments, . . . do promise to each other that they will endeavour, . . . to settle the differences so arising, and to preserve the state of peace and friendship in which the two countries are now placing themselves, using, for this end, mutual representations and pacific negotiations. . . .

Article XXI: Future disagreements between the United States and Mexico should be settled with peaceful negotiations by representatives of each country.

Article XXIII: This treaty shall be **ratified by the President of the United States of America, by and with the advice and consent of the Senate thereof;** and by the President of the Mexican Republic, with the previous approbation of its general Congress; . . . in four months from the date of the signature hereof, or sooner if practicable. . . .

Article XXIII: Treaty was to be ratified by the U.S. president with the Senate's consent and by Mexico's president and general Congress within four months of the date it was signed.

Map Study: Manifest Destiny

To complete the map on the next page, refer to the text and the maps on pages 242 and 252.

1. Put the following words or phrases under the heading that they best fit.

Bear Flag Republic	cotton crop	Nueces River
54° 40′	lumberjacks	Marcus Whitman
Nez Perce Indians	iron ore	49th parallel
Sacramento	Snake River	trappers
12,000 mile argument	Sam Houston	John C. Frémont
cattle		

Oregon	California	Texas	Maine
49th parallel	Bear Flag Republic	cotton crop	lumberjacks
Marcus Whitman	Sacramento	Sam Houston	12,000 mile argument
Nez Perce Indians	John C. Frémont	Nueces River	iron ore
Snake River		cattle	
54°40'			
trappers			

2. Label the following states and their dates of admission. (See the Appendix on page 658.)

   Indiana, Mississippi, Illinois, Alabama, Maine, Missouri, Arkansas, Michigan, Florida, Texas, Iowa, Wisconsin

3. Label the following locations.

   Alamo, Missouri River, Mississippi River, Colorado River, Columbia River, Salt Lake City, Willamette River, Rio Grande, Sacramento, Santa Fe, Snake River, 49th parallel

4. Label the following trails using the color indicated.

   Oregon Trail—blue, California Trail—red, Mormon Trail—green, Santa Fe Trail—yellow

5. Use encyclopedias to help you draw in the boundaries for the following areas related to United States expansion. Shade the areas with different colored pencils and make a key to interpret your colors.

   Louisiana Purchase, Texas (including the disputed area), Gadsden Purchase, Mexican Cession

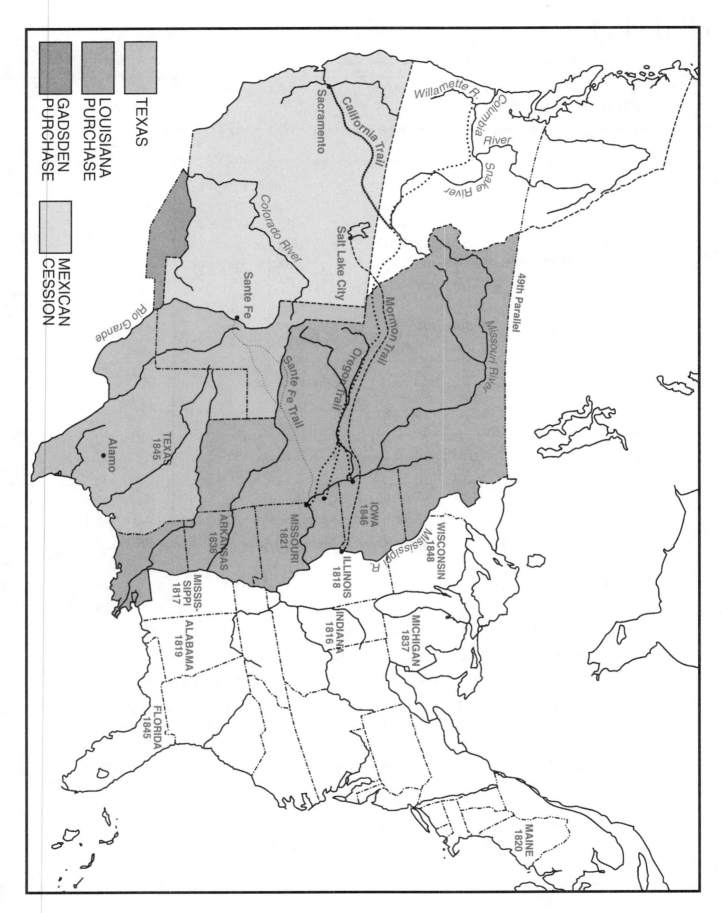

Map legend:
- GADSDEN PURCHASE
- LOUISIANA PURCHASE
- TEXAS
- MEXICAN CESSION

Willamette R.

Columbia River

Snake River

California Trail

Sacramento

49th Parallel

Colorado River

Salt Lake City

Missouri River

Mormon Trail

Rio Grande

Sante Fe

Oregon Trail

Santa Fe Trail

TEXAS 1845

Alamo

Mississippi R.

ARKANSAS 1836

MISSOURI 1821

IOWA 1846

WISCONSIN 1848

ILLINOIS 1818

MISSIS-SIPPI 1817

INDIANA 1816

MICHIGAN 1837

ALABAMA 1819

FLORIDA 1845

MAINE 1820

Viewpoint

Read and compare the following viewpoints on slavery and then answer the following questions on a separate sheet of paper.

1. Which viewpoint do you think is least accurate? Why?
2. What biases did each writer bring into his account? How are they revealed?
3. Find five Bible verses that you think apply to slavery. Give the principle expressed in each verse and explain how it could have been applied to the slave question of the 1800s.

Answers will vary. This is a good exercise to use for guided discussion.

Slave Viewpoint

The hands are required to be in the cotton field as soon as it is light in the morning and, with the exception of ten or fifteen minutes, which is given them at noon to swallow their allowance of cold bacon, they are not permitted to be a moment idle until it is too dark to see, and when the moon is full, they often times labor till the middle of the night. They do not dare to stop even at dinner time, nor return to the quarters, however late it be, until the order to halt is given by the driver.

The day's work over in the field, the baskets are "toted," or, in other words, carried to the gin-house, where the cotton is weighed. No matter how fatigued and weary he may be—no matter how much he longs for sleep and rest—a slave never approaches the gin-house with his basket of cotton but with fear. If it falls short in weight—if he has not performed the full task appointed him, he knows that he must suffer. And if he has exceeded it by ten or twenty pounds, in all probability his master will measure the next day's task accordingly.

Solomon Northup. *Twelve Years a Slave*. London: Sampson Low, 1853. Solomon Northup was a Northern free black who was drugged and sold into slavery in the South. It took twelve years to prove his case and be freed.

Owner Viewpoint

The negro slaves of the South are the happiest, and, in some sense, the freest people in the world. The children and the aged and infirm work not at all, and yet have all the comforts and necessaries of life provided for them. They enjoy liberty, because they are oppressed neither by care nor labor. The women do little hard work, and are protected from the despotism of their husbands by their masters. The negro men and stout boys work, on the average, in good weather, not more than nine hours a day. The balance of their time is spent in perfect abandon. Besides, they have their Sabbaths and holidays. White men, with so much of license and liberty, would die of ennui; but negroes luxuriate in corporeal and mental repose. With their faces upturned to the sun, they can sleep at any hour; and quiet sleep is the greatest of human enjoyments. "Blessed be the man who invented sleep." 'Tis happiness in itself—and results from contentment with the present, and confident assurance of the future.

George Fitzhugh. *Cannibals All! or Slaves Without Masters*. Richmond, Va.: A. Morris, 1857. George Fitzhugh wrote proslavery articles for the *Richmond Examiner*, a widely read Southern newspaper.

Abolitionist Viewpoint

While we bestow our earnest disapprobation on the system of slavery, let us not flatter ourselves that we are in reality any better than our brethren of the South. Thanks to our soil and climate, and the early exertions of the Quakers, the *form* of slavery does not exist among us; but the very *spirit* of the hateful and mischievous thing is here in all its strength. The manner in which we use what power we have, gives us ample reason to be grateful that the nature of our institutions does not intrust us with more. Our prejudice against colored people is even more inveterate than it is at the South. The planter is often attached to the negroes, and lavishes caresses and kind words upon them, as he would on a favorite hound: but our cold-hearted, ignoble prejudice admits of no exception—no intermission. . . .

Those who are kind and liberal on all other subjects, unite with the selfish and the proud in their unrelenting efforts to keep the colored population in the lowest state of degradation; and the influence they unconsciously exert over children early infuses into their innocent minds the same strong feelings of contempt.

Lydia Maria Child. *An Appeal in Favor of That Class of Americans Called Africans*. Boston: Allen and Ticknor, 1833.

Party Lines

Put the information below the chart under the party name to which it belongs. Some boxes will be blank.

Whigs	Republicans	Democrats	Free-Soilers	Know-Nothings
General Winfield Scott	began as an antislavery party	James Buchanan	candidate Martin Van Buren	secret societies
Zachary Taylor	Free Soil, Free Speech, Free Labor, Free Men, Frémont and Victory	divided into Northern and Southern factions	Free Soil, Free Speech, Free Labor, Free Men	Millard Fillmore
avoided adopting a party platform	Ripon, Wisconsin	Stephen Douglas		capitalized on the fear of immigrants and the Kansas-Nebraska Act
	John Brown	Franklin Pierce		
	Abraham Lincoln	Lewis Cass		

- General Winfield Scott
- Lewis Cass
- began as an antislavery party
- Ripon, Wisconsin
- James Buchanan
- secret societies
- divided into Northern and Southern factions

- Abraham Lincoln
- candidate Martin Van Buren
- John Brown
- Millard Fillmore
- Free Soil, Free Speech, Free Labor, Free Men, Frémont and Victory
- Stephen Douglas

- Free Soil, Free Speech, Free Labor, Free Men
- Zachary Taylor
- capitalized on the fear of immigrants and the Kansas-Nebraska Act
- Franklin Pierce
- avoided adopting a party platform

SKILL: Charts

Fanning the Fire

Winds of anger fanned the fires of discontent surrounding the slavery issue. The result of the flames is the mystery phrase. Put the answers to the following clues in the spaces below.

1. In this doctrine, Stephen Douglas said that a territory could prohibit slavery.
2. This fanatical antislavery proponent staged a massacre and attempted a revolt.
3. This decision declared the Missouri Compromise unconstitutional.
4. These Southern extremists wanted the South to secede to keep the Southern way of life.
5. Because of the fighting there, Kansas territory became known as this.
6. This president ran without a platform and stressed his military merits.
7. Before landing in this harbor, some captains put their crews in chains.
8. This territory's population gained 80,000 in one year.
9. This Illinois senator proposed dividing the unorganized territory in two.
10. This man found gold on his property.
11. This man made a famous speech called the "Seventh of March" speech.
12. This Southern spokesman offered resolutions that said no one could prohibit a territory from having slaves until it became a state.
13. This was the nickname given to the men who had gold rush fever.
14. They wanted to leave slavery where it was but opposed its extension into new territory.
15. This compromise made California a free state, but offered an enforced fugitive slave act.
16. This senator proposed amendments in a last effort to save the Union.
17. This was a name for the mass migration to California of men seeking wealth.
18. This act suggested the repeal of the Missouri Compromise and called for popular sovereignty in the unorganized territory.

```
                    6.                           13.        15.
                    Z                    11.      F     C    16.
              5.    A                    D        O     O    J       18.
1.   2.       B     C        9.          A  12.   R     M    O        K
F    J        L     H        S    10.    N  J     T  14. P   H        A
R    O        E     A        T    J      I  O     Y     F   N         N
E    H        E     R   7.   E    O      E  H     N     R   O    J.   S
E    N    4.  D     Y   S    P    H      L  N     I     E   M    C 17. A
P    B 3. F   I     T   A 8. H    N      W  C.    N     E   I    R  G  S
O    R  D  I  N     A   N  C E OF S  E   C  E     S     S   I    O     N
R    O  R  R  G     Y   F  A N    U  B   A  R     O     E   T    L     E
T    W  E  E  K     L   R  L D    T  S   L  S     I     O   T    D     B
D    N  D  E  A     O   A  I O    T  T   H     L  F     E   R    R
O       S  A  N     R   N  F U    E  E   O     E  1     N   U    A
C       C  T  S     C   O  G      R  R   U     R  8     D   S    S
T       O  E  A     I   R  L      N      S     5  E     H   K
R       T  R  S     S   N  A             0     N  A
I       T  S         C  I  S
N          O  A
E
```

CHAPTER REVIEW   SKILL: Comprehension   63

Crossword Puzzle

ACROSS

1. The South threatened this if Lincoln won in 1860.
5. Douglas's "Doctrine"
7. slave who was refused freedom by the Supreme Court
11. He was "honest."
12. Democratic victor in 1856
15. escape route for fugitive slaves
17. non-Republican, pro-Union party of 1860
18. site of tensions between proslavery border ruffians and antislavery free-staters
19. madman of Pottawatomie and Harpers Ferry
22. Their party split and died in the 1850s.
24. president of the Confederate States of America
25. Swiss rancher who lost his land to gold rush fever
27. destination of a rush of people in 1849
28. members of a certain antislavery political group
29. S.C. representative who broke his cane

DOWN

1. fort of first fire
2. proposed a last-minute, unsuccessful compromise
3. Constitutional Union candidate of 1860
4. senator bloodied by Brooks
6. site of Kansas massacre of proslavery settlers
7. party offering two candidates in 1860
8. famous conductor on the Underground Railroad
9. won a narrow victory in the 1848 election
10. Douglas's act introduced to promote railroad interests
13. sovereignty that let residents decide slavery issue
14. debated Douglas in 1858 and defeated him in 1860
15. influential abolitionist novel
16. state of great 1858 debates
20. His proviso failed to limit slavery in Mexican Cession.
21. Brown attempted to incite a slave revolt at this ferry.
23. wrote a successful piece of abolitionist literature
26. chief justice during Dred Scott decision

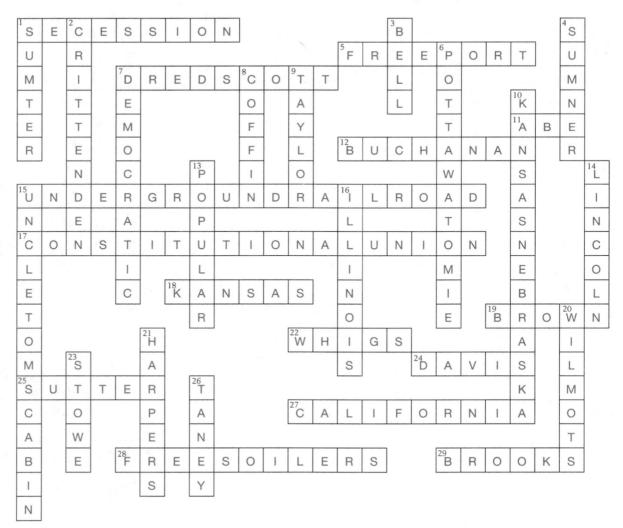

Flag Day!

Many of the troops who served in the Civil War carried high the flag of the state they represented. Use an encyclopedia to research your state flag.

1. Draw and color the blank flag below to make it look like your state flag.
   Students' answers will vary according to state. They may look in an encyclopedia under "flag" or under their specific state name.

2. What do the colors on your flag signify? _____
_____

3. What are the objects present on your state flag? _____
What do they mean? _____
_____

4. In what year was your state flag adopted in its present form? _____
_____

5. Does your flag have a motto on it? _____ If so, what does the motto mean? _____
_____
_____

6. If there are any animals on your flag, what do they represent? _____
_____

7. If your state was involved in the Civil War, which side was it on? _____
_____

8. Does your flag's design reveal which side it was on in the Civil War? _____
How? _____

Who Am I?

The following selection is a brief autobiography written in 1859. Read it and then answer the questions based on your reading.

I was born February 12, 1809, in Hardin County, Kentucky. My parents were both born in Virginia, of undistinguished families. My mother, who died in my tenth year, was of a family of the name Hanks. My paternal grandfather emigrated from Rockingham County, Virginia, to Kentucky about 1781 or 1782, where, a year or two later, he was killed by the Indians, not in battle, but by stealth when he was laboring to open a farm in the forest.

My father at the death of his father was but six years of age. By the early death of his father, and the very narrow circumstances of his mother, he was, even in childhood, a wandering laboring boy, and grew up literally without education. He never did more in the way of writing than bunglingly to write his own name. He removed from Kentucky to what is now Spencer County, Indiana, in my eighth year. It was a wild region with many bears and other animals still in the woods.

There were some schools, so-called, but no qualification was ever required of a teacher beyond "readin', writin', and cipherin' to the rule of three." If a straggler supposed to understand Latin happened to sojourn in the neighborhood he was looked upon as a wizard. Of course, when I came of age I did not know much. Still, somehow, I could read, write, and cipher to the rule of three. But that was all. The little advance I now have upon this store of education I have picked up from time to time under the pressure of necessity.

I was raised to farm work till I was twenty-two. At twenty-one I came to Illinois—Macon County. Then I got to New Salem, where I remained a year as a sort of clerk in a store. Then came the Black Hawk war; and I was elected captain of a volunteer company, a success that gave me more pleasure than any I have had since. I went into the campaign—was elated—ran for the legislature the same year (1832), and was beaten—the only time I ever have been beaten by the people. The next, and three succeeding biennial elections, I was elected to the Legislature. I was not a candidate afterward. During the legislative period I had studied law and removed to Springfield to practice it. In 1846 I was elected to the lower house of Congress. Was not a candidate for reelection. From 1849 to 1854, in politics, and generally on the Whig electoral tickets, making active canvasses. I was losing interest in politics when the repeal of the Missouri Compromise aroused me again.

If any personal description of me is thought desirable, it may be said that I am in height six feet four inches, nearly; lean in flesh, weighing on an average one hundred and eighty pounds; dark complexion, with coarse black hair and gray eyes. No other marks or brands recollected.

1. How old was the author when he wrote this autobiography? _50 years old_____

2. How did his father's father die? _His grandfather was killed by Indians._____

3. What was the author's occupation most of his early life? _He did farm work._____

4. How do you sense the author felt about the education system of his time? (Support your opinion with quotations from the excerpt.) _He doesn't seem impressed with it. He____ _uses words like "so called" and says that "no qualification was ever required of a teacher beyond___ _'readin', writin', and cipherin' to the rule of three.' "___

5. From what success did he get his greatest pleasure? _He got his greatest pleasure___ _upon being elected captain of a volunteer company.___

6. How does it appear that the author got most of his education? _on his own initiative_____

7. What was his father's occupation as a young boy? _wandering laboring boy____

8. Who is the author? ____Abraham Lincoln____ (Suggest that the students check their answers by comparing encyclopedia information about their choice with the autobiographical information above.)

Change in Southern Lifestyle

The following excerpt is from Mary Boykin Chesnut's *Diary from Dixie*. Read the entries and then answer the questions based on Mrs. Chesnut's perceptions.

RICHMOND, Va., Nov. 28, 1863.—I gave a party; Mrs. Davis very witty; Preston girls very handsome; Isabella's fun fast and furious. No party could have gone off more successfully, but my husband decides we are to have no more festivities. This is not the time, or the place, for such gaieties. . .] Mr. Venable, of Lee's staff, was at our party, so out of spirits. He knows everything that is going on. His depression bodes us no good. To-day, General Hampton sent James Chesnut a fine saddle that he had captured from the Yankees in battle array. Charleston is bombarded night and day. It fairly makes me dizzy to think of that everlasting racket they are beating about people's ears down there. Bragg defeated, and separated from Longstreet.

Nov. 30.—Anxiety pervades. Lee is fighting Meade. Misery is everywhere. Bragg is falling back before Grant. Longstreet, the soldiers call him Peter the Slow, is settling down before Knoxville. My husband bought yesterday at the commissary's one barrel of flour, one bushel of potatoes, one peck of rice, five pounds of salt beef, and one peck of salt—all for sixty dollars. In the street a barrel of flour sells for one hundred and fifteen dollars. Spent seventy-five dollars today for a little tea and sugar, and have five hundred left. [My husband laid the law down last night. I felt it to be the last drop in my full cup. "No more feasting in this house," said he. "This is no time for junketing and merry making.". . . He is the master of the house; to hear is to obey.]

December 19th.—A box has come from home for me. Taking advantage of this good fortune and full larder, have asked Mrs. Davis to dine with me. Wade Hampton sent me a basket of game. We had Mrs. Davis and Mr. and Mrs. Preston.

Christmas Day.—Yesterday dined with the Prestons. Wore one of my handsomest Paris dresses (from Paris before the war). Three magnificent Kentucky generals were present, with Senator Orr from South Carolina, and Mr. Miles. Others dropt in after dinner; some without arms, some without legs; von Borcke, who can not speak because of a wound in his throat. Isabella said: "We have all kinds now, but a blind one," Poor fellows, they laugh at wounds. "And they yet can show many a scar." We had for dinner oyster soup, besides roast mutton, ham, boned turkey, wild duck, partridge, plum pudding, sauterne, burgundy, sherry, and Madeira. There is life in the old land yet!

My husband says I am extravagant. "No, my friend, not that," said I. "I had fifteen hundred dollars and I have spent every cent of it in my housekeeping. Not one cent for myself, not one cent for dress, nor any personal want whatever." He calls me "hospitality run mad." To-day, for a pair of forlorn shoes I have paid $85. Mr. Petigru says you take your money to market in the marketbasket, and bring home what you buy in your pocketbook.

February 23d.—At the President's, where General Lee breakfasted, a man named Phelan told General Lee all he ought to do; planned a campaign for him. General Lee smiled blandly the while, tho he did permit himself a mild sneer at the wise civilians in congress who refrained from trying the battle-field in person, but from afar dictated the movements of armies.

February 26th, 1864.—We went to see Mrs. Breckenridge, who is here with her husband. Then we paid our respects to Mrs. Lee. Her room was like an industrial school; everybody so busy. Her daughters were all three plying their needles, with several other ladies. Mrs. Lee showed us a beautiful sword, recently sent to the General by some Marylanders, now in Paris. On the blade was engraved, "*Aide toi et Dieu t'aidera*." When we came out some one said, "Did you see how the Lees spend their time? What a rebuke to the taffy Parties!"

March 12th.—Somebody counted fourteen generals in church to-day, and suggested that less piety and more drilling commands would suit the times better. There were Lee, Longstreet, Morgan, Hoke, Clingman, Whiting, Pegram, Elzey, and Bragg.

March 15th.—Old Mrs. Chesnut is dead. A saint is gone and James Chesnut is broken-hearted. He adored his mother. I gave $375 for my mourning, which consists of a black alpaca dress and a crape veil. With bonnet, gloves, and all it came to $500. [Before the blockade such things as I have would not have been thought fit for a chambermaid.]Everybody is in trouble. Mrs. Davis says paper money has depreciated so much in value that they can not live within their income; so they are going to dispense with their carriage and horses.

Yesterday, we went to the Capitol grounds to see our returned prisoners. We walked slowly up and down until Jeff Davis was called upon to speak. There I stood, almost touching the bayonets when he left me.

I looked straight into the prisoners' faces, poor fellows. They cheered with all their might, and I wept for sympathy, and enthusiasm. I was deeply moved. These men were so forlorn, so dried up, and shrunken, with such a strange look in some of their eyes; others so restless and wild-looking; others again placidly vacant, as if they had been dead to the world for years.

CAMDEN, S.C., September 19th.—My pink silk dress I have sold for $600, to be paid in installments, two hundred a month for three months. And I sell my eggs and butter from home for two hundred dollars a month. Does it not sound well—four hundred dollars a month regularly. But in what? In Confederate money. Hélas!

A thousand dollars have slipped through my fingers already this week. At the commissary's I spent five hundred to-day for candles, sugar, and a lamp, etc. Tallow candles are bad enough, but of them there seems to be an end, too. Now we are restricted to smoky, terrabine lamps—terrabine is a preparation of turpentine. When the chimney of the lamp cracks, as crack it will, we plaster up the place with paper, thick old letterpaper, preferring the highly glazed kind.

Sherman is thundering at Augusta's very doors. My General was on the wing, somber, and full of care.

We have lost nearly all of our men, and we have no money, and it looks as if we had taught the Yankees how to fight since Manassas. Our best and bravest are under the sod; we should have to wait till another generation grows up. Here we stand, despair in our hearts . . . with our houses burning, or about to be, over our heads. The North have just got things ship-shape; a splendid army, perfectly disciplined, with new levies coming in day and night. Their gentry do not go into the ranks. They hardly know there is war up there.

Serena's account of money spent: Paper and envelopes, $12.00; tickets to concert, $10.00; toothbrush, $10.00; total, $32.00. To-day Mrs. McCord exchanged $16,000 in Confederate bills for $300 in gold—sixteen thousand for three hundred.

CHESTER, S.C., April 7th.—Richmond has fallen and I have no heart to write about it. Grant broke through our lines and Sherman cut through them. Stoneman is this side of Danville. They are too many for us. Everything is lost in Richmond, even our archives. Blue-black is our horizon.

April 22, 1865.—It has been a wild three days, with aides galloping around with messages, Yankees hanging over us like a sword of Damocles. We have been in queer straits.

CAMDEN, S.C., May 2, 1865.—Since we left Chester nothing but solitude, nothing but tall, blackened chimneys, to show that any man has ever trod this road before. This is Sherman's track. It is hard not to curse him. I wept incessantly at first. The roses of the gardens are already hiding the rains. My husband said Nature is a wonderful renovator. He tried to say something else and then I shut my eyes and made a vow that if we were a crusht people, crusht by weight, I would never be a whimpering, pining slave. When we crossed the river coming home, the ferryman at Chesnut's Ferry asked for his fee. Among us all we could not muster the small silver coin he demanded. There was poverty for you.

Use highlighters or colored pencils to mark the following passages.

- Underline in red the passages that show Mrs. Chesnut's extravagances in spending.

- Circle in blue the passages that reveal the low value of the Confederate currency.

- Highlight in yellow the passages that indicate how the war was actually proceeding.

- Put brackets around passages that display changes that Mrs. Chesnut made in her lifestyle. (There are several possible passages.)

- For extra credit:

   Give an approximate translation of the quotation on General Lee's sword. With the Bible as your reference point, evaluate the philosophy of the quotation.
   The translation is "Help yourself and God will help you." Discuss the balance between the Christian's responsibility to work and God's to provide.

   What was "the sword of Damocles"? Why would Mrs. Chesnut have referred to it in relation to the Confederate situation on April 22, 1865?
   Damocles was a courtier of the tyrant Dionysius in the fourth century B.C. Damocles had made some overenthusiastic statements about his sovereign's happiness. The "sword of Damocles" was a sword suspended by a thread from the ceiling over his head to make the point that the emperor Dionysius's happiness was as fragile as Damocles' life under the sword. The South's lifestyle and happiness were overshadowed by the immediate threat of Union rule.

Battle Cry!

Fill in the gaps in these major Civil War battle outlines.

I. First Battle of Manassas
   A. Other Name: First Bull Run
   B. Date: July 1861
   C. Commanders
      1. Union: Gen. Irvin McDowell
      2. Confederate: Gen. Barnard Bee
                      Gen. Thomas J. Jackson
   D. Winning Side: Confederate
   E. Strategy: straight attack on the
                Confederate line
   F. Consequences: South was relieved. North was
                    demoralized.

II. Battle of Shiloh
   A. Other Name: Pittsburgh Landing
   B. Date: April 1862
   C. Commanders
      1. Union: Gen. U. S. Grant
      2. Confederate: Gen. Albert S. Johnston
   D. Winning Side: Union
   E. Strategy: The Confederates launched a surprise
                attack on the Union line.
   F. Consequences: The Confederates were driven
                    back at great cost in human
                    lives to both sides.

III. Second Battle of Manassas
   A. Other Name: Second Bull Run
   B. Date: August 1862
   C. Commanders
      1. Union: Gen. John Pope
      2. Confederate: Gen. Robert E. Lee
                      Gen. J. E. B. Stuart
   D. Winning Side: Confederate
   E. Strategy: Lee sent Stuart around to create
                havoc at Pope's back. Jackson went
                around Pope's army, and Lee came
                down their flank.
   F. Consequences: Lee had practically driven all
                    Federal troops from Virginia.

IV. Battle of Antietam
   A. Other Name: Sharpsburg
   B. Date: September 1862
   C. Commanders
      1. Union: Gen. George B. McClellan
      2. Confederate: Gen. Robert E. Lee
   D. Winning Side: Draw
   E. Strategy: Confederates planned to disrupt
                transportation and communication by
                marching on Washington.
   F. Consequences: Battle ended in a "draw," but
                    the Union claimed victory, and
                    President Lincoln announced
                    the Emancipation
                    Proclamation.

V. Battle of Gettysburg
   A. Date: July 1863
   B. Commanders
      1. Union: Gen. George Meade
      2. Confederate: Gen. Robert E. Lee
                      Gen. George Pickett
   C. Winning Side: Union
   D. Strategy: After two days of battle, the final
                strategy was a straight Confederate
                assault on the center of the Union
                position along Cemetery Ridge.
   E. Consequences: The two sides had 50,000
                    casualties. The South would
                    never again be able to launch
                    a major offensive.

VI. Battle of Atlanta
   A. Date: July 1864
   B. Commanders
      1. Union: Gen. William T. Sherman
      2. Confederate: Gen. John B. Hood
   C. Winning Side: Union
   D. Strategy: Sherman encircled the city until the
                Confederates abandoned it.
   E. Consequences: The Union gained the South's
                    most important railroad and
                    manufacturing center.

Terms of Surrender

A series of letters were exchanged between General Lee and General Grant finalizing surrender terms at the end of the Civil War. Place yourself in the positions of each of these men and write a brief letter from each man. One letter should be from General Grant outlining the terms of surrender and the other from General Lee responding to those terms. Answers will vary.

General Grant to General Lee: _____

_____

_____

_____

_____

_____

_____

_____

_____

_____

_____

_____

_____

General Lee to General Grant:

_____

_____

_____

_____

_____

_____

_____

_____

_____

_____

_____

_____

_____

Reflections of Life

Underline the word or phrase that makes the statement correct.

1. Frenchman Louis Daguerre developed an imaging process called the *(daguerreotype, ferrotype)* which used *(enameled iron, silver-coated copper plate)* on which to capture the image.

2. *Carte-de-visite* or *(cabinet, visiting card)* photographs were small photographs that were popular to exchange with friends and family.

3. George *(Eastman, Kodak)* developed roll film, which helped make photography affordable.

4. The lifestyle of the western Indians was documented by *(Mathew Brady, Edward Curtis)* at the same time that William Henry Jackson was capturing the *(beauty of the West, atrocities of war)*.

5. *(Mathew Brady, Alexander Gardner)* photographed a dead soldier twice, moving the body so that he could call it a Union soldier and a Confederate soldier.

6. A form of home entertainment that featured three-dimensional views of faraway places was the *(triplograph, stereograph)*.

7. A turn-of-the-century camera whose improvements allowed amateurs easy loading and unloading of film was the *(Swinger, Brownie)*.

8. The first significant use of the camera in battle was during the *(Civil, Crimean)* War.

9. In the late 1830s, Louis Daguerre and *(Alfred Stieglitz, William Talbot)* developed photography independently.

10. *(Roll film, Faster shutter speed)* made it possible to market hand-held cameras.

Imagine that you are a person in one of the photographs in the chapter and write a first-person story about it.

_____

_____

_____

_____

_____

_____

_____

_____

_____

_____

_____

_____

What Do You See?

Look at the pictures on the following pages in the textbook. Give your impression of what you see in the photograph and the idea you think the photographer is trying to convey. Answers will vary. The activity may be used in a class discussion.

1. Page 321— Devil's Den, Gettysburg, July 1863 _____

   _____

   _____

   _____

   _____

2. Page 323— Ruins of Gallego Flour Mills, Richmond, Virginia, 1865 _____

   _____

   _____

   _____

   _____

3. Page 324— Mojave girl _____

   _____

   _____

   _____

   _____

4. Page 327— Girl working in textile mill _____

   _____

   _____

   _____

   _____

5. Page 328— Crowded tenement in New York slum _____

   _____

   _____

   _____

   _____

Presidential Assassinations

Refer to an encyclopedia to find information about the following presidents and their assassinations. Students' answers will vary in completeness based on the sources they use.

Abraham Lincoln

Term of Office: _1861-65_

Date of Assault: _April 14, 1865_

Assailant's name: _John Wilkes Booth_

Motive and/or mental state of the assailant: _Booth was a great supporter of the Southern cause. He also supported slavery and hated Lincoln. After he shot Lincoln, he said, "The South is avenged!"_

Effect of the assassination on the American public: _The North honored Lincoln as a martyr. Because he was assassinated on Good Friday, that Easter was known as "Black Easter." The public would never know how Lincoln's presence might have changed the Reconstruction period._

James A. Garfield

Term of Office: _1881_

Date of Assault: _July 2, 1881_

Assailant's name: _Charles J. Guiteau_

Motive and/or mental state of the assailant: _Guiteau was mentally disturbed. He wanted the Stalwarts in office. Garfield was a Half-breed, and his vice president was a Stalwart._

Effect of the assassination on the American public: _Garfield had a good start in office, so when his administration was cut off by the assassination, the public was indignant. Perhaps because of this mood, the civil service reforms Garfield had advocated were carried out._

William McKinley

Term of Office: 1897-1901

Date of Assault: September 6, 1901

Assailant's name: Leon Czolgosz

Motive and/or mental state of the assailant: Czolgosz had a history of mental instability. Because he was an anarchist, he saw all rulers as enemies of the workers.

Effect of the assassination on the American public: McKinley had just received the largest popular majority of votes ever given a presidential candidate up to that time. He was mourned greatly in the United States and abroad.

John F. Kennedy

Term of Office: 1961-63

Date of Assault: November 22, 1963

Assailant's name: Lee Harvey Oswald

Motive and/or mental state of the assailant: Oswald had a history of emotional instability. Before the assassination, he was involved with pro-Cuban and pro-Communist organizations.

Effect of the assassination on the American public: For the first time, to the shock and horror of the public, an assassination was captured on film. The American people were grief-stricken, and Kennedy was honored as a martyr and in many ways likened to Abraham Lincoln.

What precautions are now taken to protect the president? Prior to scheduled appearances, Secret Service agents inspect the area for potential dangers. Admittance to the area is often barred after the inspection until just prior to the president's arrival. The president is always attended by Secret Service members who are taught to look for possible dangers.

SKILL: Using Resources

Checking Up on Reconstruction

Show which Reconstruction plan each statement describes by placing a check in the correct box or boxes.

Lincoln's Plan
 Johnson's Plan
  Radical Republicans' Plan

✓	☐	☐	1. viewed Southerners as rebellious members of the Union
✓	✓	✓	2. decided to appoint military governors
☐	☐	✓	3. demanded the abolition of slavery
✓	✓	☐	4. believed Reconstruction was up to the president
☐	☐	✓	5. denied suffrage and political office to former Confederate leaders
☐	✓	☐	6. wanted a "ten per cent" plan with stricter qualifications
☐	☐	✓	7. promoted the Wade-Davis Bill
☐	☐	✓	8. viewed the South as conquered enemies
✓	☐	☐	9. wanted to grant presidential pardons
☐	☐	✓	10. wanted majority of Southern males to take an oath of allegiance

Take It Further

11. The Radicals made an attempt to limit the power of the president. One bill called the ___Tenure___ of ___Office___ Act was an attempt to retain ___Edwin___ ___Stanton___ as secretary of war since he was an important Radical in the cabinet.

12. How did President Johnson react to this congressional act? _He dismissed Stanton._
    What did Congress do then? _The House of Representatives impeached Johnson._
    _____

13. How would Johnson's removal have affected future presidential power? _It would_
    have made the president a servant to Congress and could have disrupted the balance of power
    between the branches of government.

14. Three amendments made during Reconstruction had consequences that reach into our twentieth-century legislation. The amendments were the ___Thirteenth___,
    ___Fourteenth___, and ___Fifteenth___.

15. Using the Appendix, pages 670-71, determine which amendment(s) the Black Codes tried to bypass and explain how they were able to do it. _The Black Codes tried to_
    bypass the Thirteenth by allowing blacks to be jailed for minor infractions (vagrancy) and thus to
    be subject to forced labor. They limited the blacks' right to serve in government, thereby taking away
    the Fourteenth (full citizenship). They denied the Fifteenth by restricting the right of blacks to vote.

Jests and Jabs

Analyze the following Nast political cartoon, taken from *The Art and Politics of Thomas Nast* by Morton Keller (Oxford University Press). Tell who the people are, whom the animals represent, and what you think Nast was trying to say.

The man is President Grant. The woman represents Liberty or perhaps the ideal United States. (Her dress should remind the students of the Statue of Liberty.) The dogs represent all of Grant's critics. (The students may be able to read the words *N. Y. Tribune* on one dog's collar. Nast actually had newspaper names on several collars.) The vultures represent the others who are waiting for President Grant's political demise. Nast is possibly saying that Grant is carrying the burden of corrupt government and unfavorable conditions down a rocky road toward political ruin. Liberty is grieved by the condition of the Union. The dogs nipping at Grant's heels further complicate his journey.

_____

_____

_____

In the box, draw a political cartoon about an issue, either state or national, that is currently in the news.

SKILL: Analysis

Exposé

Grant's administrative era was filled with political scandal within and without. Summarize the following scandals using the terms given.

The Tammany Hall Scandal

Tammany Hall was a political organization originally started in the late 1700s to protect poorer citizens from the control of those with property. It later became an organization of the middle class which, when property qualifications for voting were lifted, began to take control of the New York City government. How did Tammany Hall's control affect New York? *(Terms: "Boss" Tweed, corruption, bribes, cartoons, reform)*

Under the control of William "Boss" Tweed, Tammany Hall's influence grew until it controlled most of New York's political process. The political corruption was so rampant under Tweed's leadership that he and the other Tammany leaders were able to embezzle millions of dollars from New York City, causing the city's debt to rise from $36 million to more than $136 million. Hospitals, asylums, and other institutions that were to benefit the people existed only on paper. Because of Tweed's power, fellow Democrats were willing to ignore the corruption, and Tweed was able to keep the Republicans under control with bribes. As reform came, Tweed's greatest foe became the cartoons drawn by Thomas Nast. Tweed knew that his uneducated supporters could not read editorials but could understand Nast's opposition cartoons.

The Credit Mobilier Scandal

This scandal occurred when Credit Mobilier managed to buy the outstanding stock of the Union Pacific Railroad and reissue it to Credit Mobilier stockholders so that both companies had the same owners. How did they make money this way and keep from being investigated? *(Terms: market value, Schuyler Colfax, 1872)*

By padding its construction expenses, the Credit Mobilier construction company was able to give the excess money to its stockholders, many of whom were also Union Pacific officers. It was able to prevent investigation by selling stock far below market value to congressmen and other government officials. When congressional investigation finally came in 1872, it was disclosed that shares were received not only by important Republicans but also by Vice President Schuyler Colfax.

The Gold Scandal

This scandal occurred when two men tried to gain control of the gold supply. How did they plan to make a profit from this scheme, and why was their attempt unsuccessful? *(Terms: Fisk and Gould, federal treasury, Black Friday)*

James Fisk and Jay Gould planned to buy enough gold on the New York Stock Exchange to force the price of gold to rise. When it had risen, they intended to sell the gold at a considerable profit. Their plan depended on preventing the federal treasury from selling any of its gold reserves; therefore, they convinced President Grant that inflation would result if any federal gold was sold. On September 24, 1869, "Black Friday," they began their plan, but when Grant discovered their scheme, he ordered the release of federal gold for sale. The Fisk-Gould plan only partially succeeded.

The Whiskey Ring Scandal

This scandal involved one of Grant's closest acquaintances. Who was this acquaintance, and how was this scandal carried out? *(Terms: excise taxes, character witness, tax collectors)*

The acquaintance was Grant's private secretary, Orville Babcock. In this scandal, whiskey distillers and federal tax collectors tried to cheat the government out of millions of dollars in excise tax revenues. Grant did not want a very thorough investigation because of his close ties with his secretary and even went so far as to testify as a character witness for Babcock.

REINFORCEMENT: Section III   SKILL: Writing   77

Presidential Insights

The following are quotes from President Rutherford B. Hayes's *Diary and Letters.* **What insights do the quotes give concerning the nineteenth president of the United States?** Answers will vary. The activity may be used in a class discussion.

1. **As a college student:** It is another intention of mine, that after I have commenced in life, whatever may be my ability or station, to preserve a reputation for honesty and benevolence; and if ever I am a public man I will never do anything inconsistent with the character of a true friend and good citizen. To become such a man I shall necessarily have to live in accordance with the precepts of the Bible, which I firmly believe, although I have never made them strictly the "rule of my conduct.". . .

   Insight— Set goals for his life. Desired to be honest, generous, a true friend, and a good citizen and
   to live in accordance with biblical principles.

2. **On marriage:** The dear friend who is to share with me the joys and ills of our earthly being grows steadily nearer and dearer to me. A better wife I never hope to have. . . . Let me strive to be as true to her as she is to me. . . .

   Insight— Looked at his wife as a friend to share life with and determined to be true to her.
   Appreciated her.

3. **On the birth of his first child:** For the "lad" my feeling has yet to grow a great deal. I prize him and rejoiced to have him, and when I take him in my arms begin to feel a father's love and interest, hope and pride, enough to know what feeling will be if not what it is. . . .

   Insight— Rejoiced to have his child but realized he was just beginning to love his son.

4. **On joining the army for the Civil War:** This was a just and necessary war and . . . it demanded the whole power of the country; . . . I would prefer to go into it if I knew I was to die or be killed in the course of it, than to live through and after it without taking any part in it. . . .

   Insight— Thought this war was justified and necessary. Had a high standard of honor; would
   rather be killed than not to fight.

5. **On politics:** Nothing brings out the lower traits of human nature like office-seeking. Men of good character and impulses are betrayed by it into all sorts of meanness.

   Insight— Thought politics brought out the worst in men.

6. **On Christianity:** I am not a subscriber to any creed. . . . I try to be a Christian. . . . I want to be a Christian and to help do Christian work. . . .

   Insight— Said he wanted to be a Christian and tried to be a Christian and do Christian work.

SKILLS: Analysis and Evaluation

Building a Monopoly

A monopoly occurs when one person, business, or organization has complete control over a commercial activity. The following are six forms of monopolies. Put the letter of the monopoly next to the examples that match it.

A. horizontal integration: One company totally controls one level of production.

B. vertical integration: One company controls all aspects of production from start to finish.

C. trust: Several companies join their stock into one trust which controls prices.

D. pooling: Two or more competing companies share profits, thus eliminating competition.

E. holding company: Two or more companies give 51 percent of their stock to a holding company. The major stockholders in the individual companies also hold stock in the holding company. Since the holding company is not producing anything and has no management expenses, when it sells its own stock, the money it makes is total profit to all the stockholders involved.

F. interlocking directorates: Two or more companies have the same board of directors, thereby reducing competition.

___A___ 1. The Crazy Cracker Company owns all the cracker-baking facilities in the U.S.

___E___ 2. Even though the Matthews Corporation doesn't produce anything under that name, it does sell stock and actually holds majority stock in three other companies.

___C___ 3. The Click Railway and Clack Lines have decided to join their stock into a corporation called Clickety Clack Tracks. Each company will retain its name but will now get the profits from both companies.

___F___ 4. My annual stock reports show that the board of directors in three of the companies is identical.

___B___ 5. The Laughing Gas Company owns 70 percent of the petroleum production process from exploration to refining to sales. They laugh all the way to the bank.

___C___ 6. Three car manufacturers joined under the name Conglomerate Motors to unify pricing and increase profits.

___A___ 7. Woof and Warp Weavers has the only factory in America that can weave argyle socks.

___B___ 8. Mr. Clark owns the Comer Bicycle Shop. He also owns the steel mill, bicycle factory, and tire company. No one else in town sells bikes.

___D___ 9. My town has two fast-food restaurants. After several price wars, they decided to work together. Now when one runs a special, the other gets part of the profit. Our hamburgers cost more these days.

___E___ 10. The Balius Trucking Company and Creason Transport both gave 51 percent of their stock to a company named BC Trucking. BC Trucking sells its own stock, and the profits go to stockholders from both companies.

___A___ 11. Turner Heating and Air Conditioning is the only installation and repair company in town. Mr. Turner charges whatever price he wants for his services.

___F___ 12. The Credit Mobilier company from the previous chapter changed its corporate structure to get more profits.

Men Who Made a Difference

Use an encyclopedia to find the contribution made by each of the following men, and then answer the questions.

George Eastman

What are the dates of his birth and death? July 12, 1854 / March 14, 1932

What was his other occupation? bookkeeper

Name his first invention and the year he invented it. flexible film, 1884

Name his second invention and the year he invented it. a box camera (the Kodak),1889

How did it affect American life? Individuals could record daily life on film. It allowed historians to keep more accurate visual records of history.

After his success, Eastman gave money to what type of institutions? He gave to technical institutes and universities.

Charles Martin Hall

What are the dates of his birth and death? December 6, 1863 / December 27, 1914

What was the date of his contribution? February 23, 1886

What was his contribution? an electrolytic process to isolate aluminum from other compounds

How did the invention affect American life? Students' answers will vary. They should realize that aluminum is lightweight and versatile. They may name some products that have resulted (e.g., aluminum cans, aluminum cookware).

What company became the first producer of aluminum? Pittsburgh Reduction Company, later named the Aluminum Company of America

What special honor did Hall receive? the Perkins Medal

Elisha Otis

What are the dates of his birth and death? August 3, 1811 / April 8, 1861

What was the year of his contribution? 1852

What was his contribution? an elevator with a safety device to prevent a sudden fall even if the cable was cut

What later improvement did he make to his contribution? He developed a steam-driven elevator.

What were two other inventions attributed to him? Students' answers will vary. He also invented railroad car brakes, the rotary oven, the steam plow, and a safety bridge.

How did his contribution affect American life? His contribution, through his sons, allowed elevators to be safely used in tall buildings; these buildings may not have been built without his contribution.

Charting America's Growth

Using the following table, make a line graph of the growth patterns in the five major U.S. cities. Use colored pencils or markers to make your lines match the color indicated below the city name. (These numbers show population changes within city limits. Population declines may be due to migration to suburban areas.)

	New York (blue)	Los Angeles (red)	Chicago (green)	Houston (black)	Philadelphia (yellow)
1850	696,115	1,610	29,963	2,396	121,376
1900	3,437,202	102,479	1,698,575	44,633	1,293,697
1950	7,891,957	1,970,358	3,620,962	596,163	2,071,605
1960	7,781,984	2,479,015	3,550,404	938,219	2,002,512
1970	7,895,563	2,811,801	3,369,357	1,233,535	1,949,996
1980	7,071,639	2,966,850	3,005,072	1,595,138	1,688,210
1990	7,428,162	3,485,557	2,783,726	1,654,348	1,585,577
2000	8,008,278	3,694,820	2,896,016	1,953,631	1,517,550

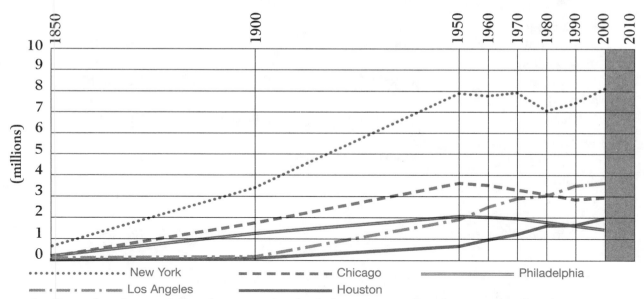

1. Extend each population line into the shaded area to predict the growth of each city to the year 2010 based on the information given. Lines will vary but should continue in a direction and pitch consistent with the established line.

2. Which two cities continued to grow during the recorded period? _Houston and Los Angeles_

3. What do you think caused the growth in those two cities? _Answers will vary but may_ include the following: increased employment opportunities, the oil industry boom in Houston, and increased immigration into Los Angeles.

The Gilded Age

In each numbered line, underline the word(s) least related to the bold word.

1. **realism**
   Call of the Wild   Twain   Homer   <u>helpless man</u>

2. **Jack London**
   <u>Horatio Alger</u>   naturalism   Darwinism   Stephen Crane

3. **Social Darwinism**
   survival of the fittest   competition   Rockefeller   <u>cooperation</u>

4. **croquet**
   <u>baseball</u>   tennis   golf   bicycling

5. **profit**
   decorations   <u>Jumbo</u>   Woolworth   materialism

6. **Moody**
   urban evangelism   Sam Jones   gospel songs   <u>Spencer</u>

7. **Sankey**
   "Jesus Is Calling"   Moody   <u>blind</u>   gospel songs

8. **Carnegie**
   <u>horizontal integration</u>   philanthropy   steel   textile mill

9. **Rockefeller**
   horizontal integration   trust   Standard Oil   <u>bobbin boy</u>

10. **Vanderbilt**
    steamboats   Commodore   railroads   <u>steel</u>

11. **Morgan**
    <u>philanthropy</u>   stocks   300-ft. yacht   mergers

12. **Duke**
    marketing strategy   tobacco   <u>steel</u>   hydroelectricity

13. **Heinz**
    Pure Food & Drug Act   honesty   Christianity   <u>financier</u>

14. **mass production**
    standardized sizing   sewing machine   <u>tailors</u>   democratization

15. **communication revolution**
    business growth   typewriter   shorthand   <u>telegraph</u>

16. **Stalwarts**
    <u>favored reform</u>   hard money   high tariffs   spoils system

17. **Cleveland**
    Mugwumps   <u>Conkling</u>   mudslinging   Blaine

18. **Farmer's Alliance**
    Oliver Kelly   <u>strikes</u>   Grange railroad   regulation

19. **William Jennings Bryan**
    <u>"goldbugs"</u>   "Great Commoner"   Christian   Populist party

20. **free silver**
    People's party   farmers   inflation   <u>gold</u>

                                                                SKILL: Application

Map Study: Routes and Riches

Refer to the map on pages x-xi of the text and a United States atlas to complete the map on the next page. Label all states west of the Mississippi River with their postal abbreviations found in the Appendix on page 658.

1. Using the directions below, show the approximate route of the major railroads given. Label the railroad lines and the cities mentioned.
   - Great Northern—Fargo, North Dakota; north to Grand Forks, North Dakota; west along the northern borders of North Dakota and Montana; south to Spokane, Washington; west ending in Seattle, Washington
   - Northern Pacific—Duluth, Minnesota; to Fargo, North Dakota; west to the southern border of Montana; following the border northwest to Butte, Montana; crossing Idaho at the 48th parallel; through Spokane, Washington; then dipping southwest before ending in Tacoma, Washington
   - Union & Central Pacifics—Omaha, Nebraska; west along the Platte River to Cheyenne, Wyoming; to the east side of the Great Salt Lake; around the northern end of the Great Salt Lake; southwest to Sacramento, California; ending in San Francisco, California. Mark the map with an "X" at Promontory Point where the two lines joined.
   - Southern Pacific—New Orleans, Louisiana; west to San Antonio, Texas; to the Rio Grande; northwest to El Paso, Texas; west to Tucson, Arizona; northwest to the Gila River; west to Yuma, Arizona; northwest ending in Los Angeles, California

2. Draw the approximate routes of the following cattle trails. Use colored pencils according to the color given next to each trail name. Label the routes and cities mentioned.
   - Goodnight-Loving Trail (blue)—Central Texas near the Colorado River; west to Pecos, Texas; north through New Mexico to Denver, Colorado; ending in Cheyenne, Wyoming
   - Western Trail (red)—north of San Antonio, Texas; north to the Texas border; northwest to Dodge City, Kansas; northwest ending in Ogallala, Nebraska
   - Chisholm Trail (green)—south of San Antonio, Texas (east of the Western Trail); north to Abilene, Kansas
   - Sedalia Trail (yellow)—south of San Antonio, Texas (east of Chisholm Trail); north to Fort Worth, Texas; northeast to Sedalia, Missouri

3. Identify the following mining areas with their names. Next to the name, draw a yellow nugget if gold was mined, a gray nugget if silver was mined, and an orange nugget if copper was mined.
   - Pikes Peak, Colorado
   - Leadville, Colorado
   - Comstock Lode (south of Virginia City, Nevada)
   - Anaconda, Montana

4. Identify the early major meat-packing plant locations with the city name and a small cow. 🐄
   - Chicago, Illinois
   - Milwaukee, Wisconsin
   - Cincinnati, Ohio
   - Minneapolis, Minnesota

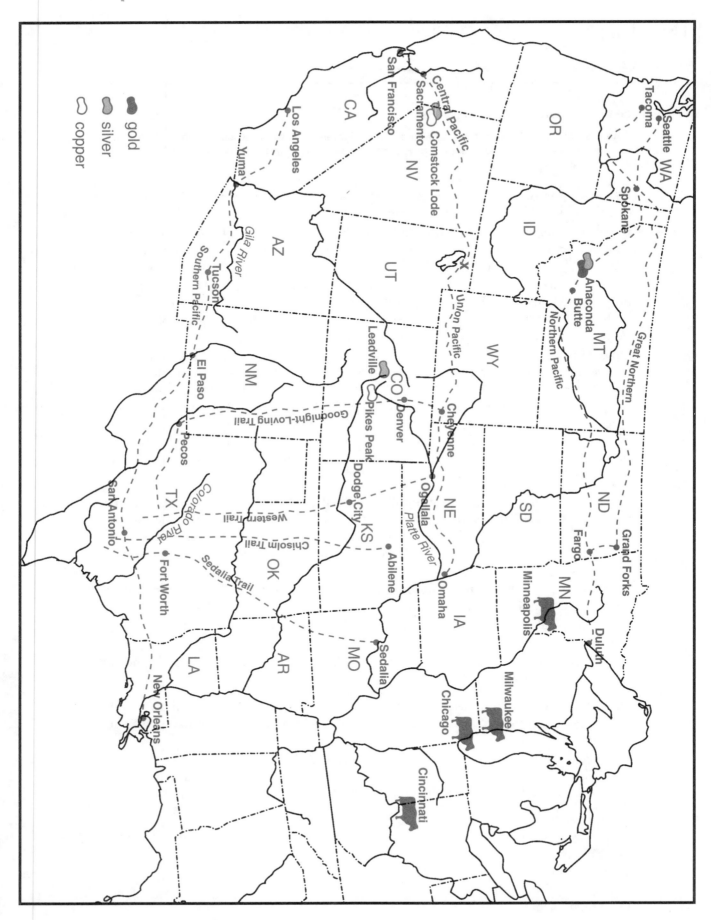

Farming Fluctuations

Use the following information to build three bar graphs showing the fluctuation in farming. Use markers or colored pencils. Use green for farmers, red for farms, and brown for acres. Optional Activity: Answer the questions on the next page using the graphs.

Year	Total Farmers (x 1,000)	Total Farms (x 1,000)	Total Acres (x 1,000)
1880	21,973	4,009	536,082
1890	24,771	4,565	623,219
1900	29,875	5,740	841,202
1910	32,077	6,366	881,431
1920	31,974	6,564	958,677
1930	30,529	6,295	990,112
1940	30,547	6,102	1,065,114
1950	23,048	5,388	1,161,420
1960	15,635	3,962	1,176,946
1970	9,712	2,954	1,102,769

Total Farmers *(x 1,000)*

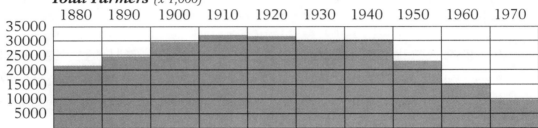

Total Farms *(x 1,000)*

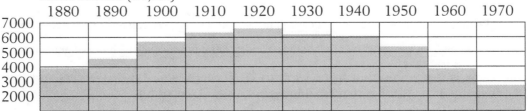

Total Acres *(x 1,000)*

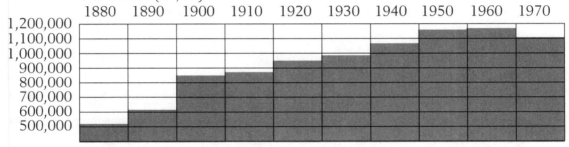

Agricultural Assimilation

Use the previous activity and the book to answer the following questions. You may need to go to other sources or ask your parents or grandparents for input. This exercise will be good for discussion. The students will have to do much research to come up with conclusive answers.

1. What decade shows the greatest numerical increase in farms, farmers, and total acres? What are some possible reasons for that increase?

   The decade from 1890 to 1900 shows the greatest increase in all areas. This probably was due to

   the dramatic increase in population because of immigration.

   _____

2. Which decade had the most numerical stability in all areas? Why could this have occurred?

   The decade from 1930 to 1940 shows the greatest stability. This could have occurred because of

   the depression. Those who had farms tended to stay put. Because of the depression, few people

   could afford to buy new farms.

3. What decade shows a sharp decline in farms and farmers? What event occurred prior to that time that may have begun the decline and yet allowed an increase in farmed acres? How do you think that event affected the decline and yet allowed the increase?

   The decade from 1940 to 1950 shows the greatest decline. World War II began, thereby taking away

   young men who would have started new farms or taken over their parents' farms. Technology

   allowed for the increase in production. Also, need stimulated production because the United States

   was providing for its armed services and for much of Europe's food needs.

4. Based on the decades from 1950 to 1970, what can we assume happened to farmers and farms from 1970 to 1990?

   Because there is a consistent decline in farmers and farms, we can assume the decline continued.

   It can also be assumed that technology allowed more productivity with less manual labor.

5. How is it possible that from 1950 to 1970 there were fewer farmers and farms and yet the amount of acreage being farmed remained stable?

   The increases in technology gained from World War II and the space race combined to improve

   machinery. More was done with chemical fertilizers and weed killers. Less work was needed to

   harvest as much acreage, so it remained stable.

6. Why are there so many farmers and farms in 1880 and 1890 in comparison to the acreage they farmed? What does this tell about the shift in occupations in the United States in the past one hundred years?

   Because farming was done with animals and hand implements, it took much longer to cultivate and

   harvest the acreage owned. Farmers couldn't work as much land, so there was room for more of

   them. Now there are fewer farmers working more land, which shows a shift from agrarian to industrial

   and technological jobs.

SKILLS: Graphs and Using Resources

Cartoon Comments

Political cartoons are used to put a big message into a little package. Answer the following questions about the cartoons on pages 395 and 401 in the text.

Page 395

1. Which character represents the United States in this cartoon? <u>Uncle Sam</u>

2. How does the cartoon make you feel about the position that the United States is taking in this issue? <u>Answers will vary—proud, unselfish, responsible, protective.</u>

3. What countries is Uncle Sam holding back? <u>Germany, France, Russia, Italy</u>

4. What do their intentions seem to be? Are they friendly or aggressive? <u>They seem to want to take over by force or kill the Chinese. They appear very aggressive.</u>

5. What country is represented by the man in the background tipping his hat? What does his action signify? Why isn't he standing closer? <u>The country represented is Great Britain. The hat tipping signifies agreement with United States policy. He doesn't want to get too involved.</u>

6. What is being offered by the U.S. Commercial Expansion? <u>railroads and other commerce</u>

7. How is the Chinese man portrayed? What does his attitude seem to be? <u>The Chinese man is portrayed as an older, wiser businessman. He is undisturbed, perhaps even smug, as he examines the merchandise that is being offered.</u>

8. Write a one- or two-sentence statement on how you think this cartoon would have influenced your opinions of the Open Door Policy. <u>Answers will vary.</u>

Page 401

9. What are the countries on the menu from which Uncle Sam may choose? <u>Cuba, Puerto Rico, the Philippines, and the Sandwich islands</u>

10. Look in an outside source to find the present name of the Sandwich Islands. <u>Hawaii</u>

11. Who is waiting to take Uncle Sam's order? <u>President McKinley</u>

12. Use one word to describe how Uncle Sam appears to feel about the choices on the menu? <u>Answers will vary—superior, smug, satisfied.</u>

13. Write a one- or two-sentence description of how the United States acquired each of the countries listed on the bill of fare. <u>The United States acquired Cuba as a protectorate at the end of the Spanish-American War. It acquired Puerto Rico just before the end of the war as a final event to force the Spanish to sue for peace. The United States acquired the Philippines in war concessions with Spain. The United States annexed Hawaii just prior to the Spanish-American War to maintain a Pacific base of operations.</u>

14. Write a one- or two-sentence statement on how you think this cartoon would have influenced your opinions of United States imperialism. <u>Answers will vary.</u>

Time Tells All

Put the correct letter from the time line next to the term. Letters may be used more than once. In the other blank, give a short explanation of the term.

__K__ 1. annexation of Hawaii _taken as a Pacific base for Spanish-American War_

__G__ 2. *A Century of Dishonor* _written by Helen Hunt Jackson to show ill treatment of Indians_

__E__ 3. Custer's Last Stand _200 soldiers against 2,000 Indians—Battle of Little Bighorn_

__K__ 4. the *Maine* sunk _unexplained event which helped lead to the Spanish-American War_

__B__ 5. Alaska purchase _known as Seward's Folly—purchased from Russia for $7.2 million_

__A__ 6. Treaty of Kanagawa _major victory for American trade—helped open Japan to trading_

__J__ 7. Wounded Knee Massacre _Soldiers killed 150 Sioux. (Half were women and children.)_

__H__ 8. founding of CMA _Christian Missionary Alliance founded by A. B. Simpson_

__K__ 9. Battle of Manila Bay _Americans wrecked the Spanish fleet and drove Spain from the Pacific_

__M__ 10. Boxer Rebellion _Chinese antiforeign movement begun by the Righteous and Harmonious Fists_

__I__ 11. First Pan-American Congress _sought greater cooperation and unity in the Western world_

__C__ 12. Battle of the Washita River _typical battle strategy of Custer—divided his troops to attack_

__D__ 13. Treaty of Washington _settled questions between United States and Canada and Britain_

__H__ 14. Dawes Act _allowed Indian lands to be parceled out to individuals and used as they desired_

__J__ 15. founding of CAM _Central American Mission founded by C. I. Scofield_

__K__ 16. Spanish-American War _begins when Spain refused to withdraw from Cuba when asked_

__F__ 17. surrender of Chief Joseph _occurred after the Nez Perce tribe tried to flee to Canada_

__L__ 18. Open Door Policy proposed _wanted all nations to have free trade in China_

__B__ 19. annexation of Midway _taken as part of U.S. Pacific empire build-up_

__N__ 20. Indian citizenship _given to redress some of the wrongs done to the Indians_

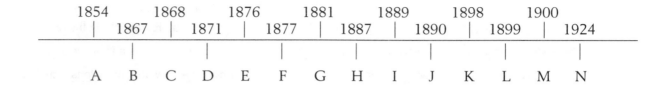

1854	1868	1876	1881	1889	1898	1900	
1867	1871	1877	1887	1890	1899	1924	
A	B	C	D	E	F	G	H	I	J	K	L	M	N

Into the Sunset

Complete the following narrative passage.

Many of the stories told about the cowboys of the Wild West are more rumor than reality. Wild West heroes such as James Butler Hickok, better known as (1) "___Wild___ ___Bill___" were actually cold-blooded killers. Law and order were needed on the frontier, but because the cowboys lived on the edge of Indian territory, the law often did not reach them. When it did, it took many forms. The low man on the law enforcement ladder was the (2) ___town marshal___. Next came the county sheriff, who was able to appoint (3) ___deputies___ to serve under him. Finally there were U.S. marshals and judges, who were directly commissioned by the president. The most famous of these judges was (4) ___Isaac Charles Parker___, also known as the (5) "___Hanging___ Judge." Many times there were still not enough lawmen to protect so large a territory. The (6) ___Wells Fargo___ shipping company suffered over (7) ___two hundred___ stage-coach robberies in one month. They hired the famous (8) ___Pinkerton___ National Detective Agency, which developed the first (9) "___most-wanted___" file. We often think of the stage-coach bandit with a bandana over the bottom half of his face, but the cowboy most often wore the bandana, or (10) ___neckerchief___, to keep the dust out of his nose and mouth when he trailed the herd. From head to toe, the cowboy was dressed for the job of herding cattle. His "Stetson" kept the sun and the rain off his head, and, though it did hold water, it couldn't really hold a full (11) ___ten gallons___. His boots were narrow at the top to keep (12) ___rocks and dirt___ out and pointed in the toe so he could slip in and out of his (13) ___stirrups___ easily. Although he had planned to make tents with it, (14) ___Levi Strauss___ found that the *serge de Nimes*, or (15) ___denim___, that he had purchased could endure the tough wear of the cowboy. Blue jeans became the staple of the working cowboy. But not all cowboys rode the range. Bill Cody, bet-ter known as (16) ___Buffalo Bill___, found that people would pay to see the romantic image of the West. Thousands of people came to see the Indian chief (17) ___Sitting Bull___ and the little woman (18) ___Annie Oakley___, who could shoot a dime tossed in the air. People liked this romantic West so much that they wanted to read about it. In 1902, Owen Wistar wrote (19) ___The Virginian___, a novel that set the western stereotypes for several decades. Two other authors, (20) ___Zane Grey___ and (21) ___Louis L'Amour___, took over where Wistar left off to become the best-known western novelists. Our perception of the Old West has also been shaped by the movie and television industry. The first western movie was (22) ___The Great Train Robbery___. The 1930s' singing cowboy, (23) ___Gene Autry___, became an example of good behavior. This was quite a switch from the reality of the Old West.

ENRICHMENT: Review   SKILL: Vocabulary   89

"Who Should Go West?"

After the deaths of his wife and mother, Theodore Roosevelt moved to the Dakota Badlands to become a rancher. The following is an excerpt from Roosevelt's book "Who Should Go West." List the qualities Roosevelt thought those going West should possess and explain what you think Roosevelt means. Answers will vary. The activity may be used as part of a class discussion.

To be able to follow the business at all, the man must be made of fairly stern stuff. He must be stout and hardy; he must be quick to learn, and have a fair share of dogged resolution; and must rapidly accustom himself to habits of complete self-reliance. If he wishes to lead a happy life, he must also be good-natured, for his companions will greet with the most merciless raillery the slightest timidity or clumsiness on the part of a beginner, and they are a class of men who will resent in the roughest and most effectual manner any exhibition of ill temper. Even after many months of patient practice it is rare that an Eastern-bred man attains to the perfection shown by the plainsman in the actual cow-boy work, such as throwing the rope, stopping a stampede, breaking a rough horse, etc. To make up for his shortcomings in these particulars, he must show especial excellence in other regards. He must work regularly, not by spasms; he must keep sober; must be always alert and ready, and willing to turn his hand to whatever comes up.

	Roosevelt's Phrasing	*Interpretation*
1.	made of fairly stern stuff	firm, unyielding, uncompromising
2.	stout and hardy	bold or brave and having good health
3.	quick to learn	ability to understand and perform tasks rapidly
4.	dogged resolution	stubbornly persevering determination
5.	complete self-reliance	ability to be totally independent
6.	good-natured	cheerful; ability to laugh at one's self
7.	work regularly	life characterized by consistent work
8.	keep sober	does not habitually drink alcoholic beverages
9.	alert and ready	vigilantly attentive and prepared to respond
10.	willing to turn his hand to whatever comes up	ready to do whatever needs to be done

Progressive Terms

Write the terms that complete the statements.

1. The nomination of a party's candidate by popular vote is called ____direct primary____.

2. A petition to hold an election to remove an elected official from office is ____recall____.

3. A person or business that controls distribution and prices of a product or service is a _____monopoly_____.

4. A man who serves as an administrator of city government is called a ____city manager____.

5. People voting yes or no to accept or reject a law is a ____referendum____.

6. Placing the power of government in the hands of the people is ____direct democracy____.

7. City government that combines the duties of mayor and city council and gives them to a group of men is called _____city commission_____.

8. A form of government control designed to break up existing monopolies is called _____gas and water socialism_____.

9. A process in which voters introduce legislation by petitioning their legislators to consider some action is _____initiative_____.

10. Reform through direct government action is government ____intervention____.

11. Breaking up monopolies and restoring competition to the marketplace is _____trust busting_____.

12. The voting method that reduced voter intimidation was the ____secret ballot____.

13. One of the means of progressive reform was increasing ____government____ efficiency.

14. The ideological movement favoring political and social reform through education, all class political participation, and direct government action was ____progressivism____.

15. Writers who exposed abuse and corruption were ____muckrakers____.

16. Banning the manufacture, sale, and transportation of alcoholic beverages is ____prohibition____.

17. Progressives favored legislation that allowed _____labor unions_____ to organize and force businesses to negotiate fairly.

18. To ____reform Darwinists____, progress was a process of the natural order that could be aided by government intervention.

19. Historian Tindall stated, "The cure for the ills of democracy was ____more democracy____."

20. Roosevelt was said to be in some ways the most "____aristocratic____" president since John Adams.

Think About It!

Give a short definition of each amendment listed and tell how it changed the previous system and what effects it has had since. Tell whether you agree or disagree with the amendment and be ready to defend your opinion. You may refer to the Appendix on page 671 and other sources.

1. Sixteenth Amendment: It gave Congress the power to tax income without regard for state population or national census. Prior to this time, the government got its funds from tariffs and would make cuts in spending when there wasn't enough tariff money available. When Wilson established the first income tax, it became an unlimited source so that Congress would increase taxes rather than cut spending to attempt to balance the budget. This process led to a pattern of using next year's taxes to clear last year's debt.

2. Seventeenth Amendment: This amendment established that the two senators from each state would be elected directly by the people in a popular vote. Prior to this time, senators were appointed by state legislatures, causing widespread abuse of the system in the form of bribery. Now senators are elected in what often amounts to a popularity contest. Many times voters are poorly informed about the issues and the candidates' views on them. Because of voter apathy, many times the candidate is elected by the minority viewpoint rather than the majority.

3. Eighteenth Amendment: This amendment banned the manufacture, sale, or transport of alcoholic beverages. The previous situation was much like today—very few restrictions on the alcohol industry. Correctly, progressives saw alcohol as a major contributor to social problems such as abuse, crime, and unemployment. However, they failed to see the basic need of man— salvation through Jesus Christ. Until the heart is changed, the same sin problems will manifest themselves. This amendment was later repealed.

4. Nineteenth Amendment: This amendment gave women suffrage. Prior to this time, only men had the right to vote. Women today have a greater voice in the government, not only through voting but also by holding public office.

Cryptograms

Use the clues to decode the words below. Then use the code to read the quotation at the bottom.

1. Roosevelt's platform against Taft and Wilson
   NEW   NATIONALISM
   YGV   YDNWCYDBWHR

2. Roosevelt's foreign policy
   SPEAK   SOFTLY   AND   CARRY   A   BIG   STICK
   HIGDF   HCZNBO   DYQ   KDEEO   D   MWL   HNWKF.

3. Roosevelt refused to shoot a captured bear, and this was the result.
   THE   TEDDY   BEAR
   NAG   NGQQO   MGDE

4. fair treatment and equal opportunity for men and women
   SQUARE   DEAL
   HJPDEG   QGDB

5. The Northern Securities case gave Roosevelt this name.
   TRUST-BUSTER
   NEPHN-MPHNGE

6. the Progressive party nickname
   THE   BULL   MOOSE   PARTY
   NAG   MPBB   RCCHG   IDENO

7. Roosevelt's name for the writers who exposed abuse and corruption
   MUCKRAKERS
   RPKFEDFGEH

8. Roosevelt's answer to the comment that his conservation policy would be a memorial to him
   BULLY,   I'D   RATHER   HAVE   IT   THAN   A HUN-
   MPBBO,   W'Q   EDNAGE   ADSG   WN   NADY   D APY-
   DRED   STONE   MONUMENTS.
   QEGQ   HNCYG   RCYPRGYNH.

9. Roosevelt did this in the election of 1912.
   THREW   HIS   HAT   INTO   THE   RING
   NAEGV   AWH   ADN   WYNC   NAG   EWYL

Presidents are people too. Although he was head of the nation, Roosevelt had this to say about his eldest daughter when he was asked if he could control her better.
   I   CAN DO   ONE   OF   TWO   THINGS;   I   CAN   BE
   W   KDY QC   CYG   CZ   NVC   NAWYLH,   W   KDY   MG
   PRESIDENT   OF   THE   UNITED   STATES   OR   I
   IEGHWQGYN   CZ   NAG   PYWNGQ   HNDNGH   CE   W
   CAN   CONTROL   ALICE.   I   CANNOT   POSSIBLY
   KDY   KCYNECB   DBWKG.   W   KDYYCN   ICHHWMBO
   DO   BOTH.
   QC   MCNA

Map Study: Roosevelt Corollary

Refer to the map on pages xii-xiii of the text and a world atlas to complete the map below.

1. Label these countries with abbreviations:
   Cuba (CU), Mexico (MX), Haiti (HA), Virgin Islands (VI), Dominican Republic (DR), Puerto Rico (PR), Belize (BE), Guatemala (GU), El Salvador (ES), Costa Rica (CR), Honduras (HO), Panama (PN), Colombia (CL), Venezuela (VE), Nicaragua (NI). (Belize was known as British Honduras prior to 1981.)

2. Using a green pencil, color the country that controlled Panama prior to its independence.

3. Using a red pencil, color the country that was an alternate location for an Atlantic-Pacific canal.

4. Using a blue pencil, draw in the Panama Canal and label it.

5. Using a yellow pencil, color the country that became a commonwealth of the United States in 1898.

6. Using a purple pencil, color the two countries that were occupied by a U.S. Marine police force during Woodrow Wilson's presidency. (See page 448 of the text.)

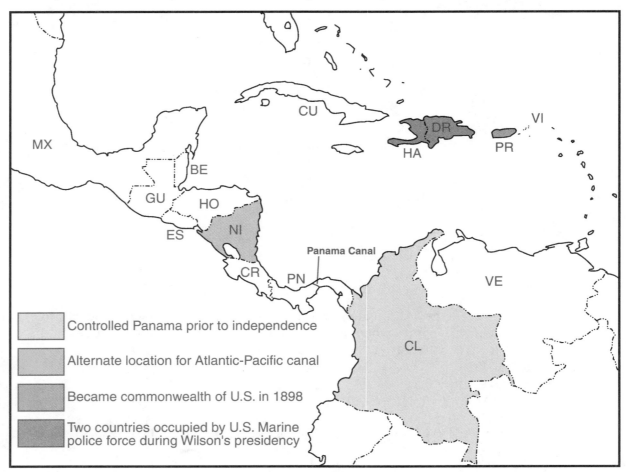

Controlled Panama prior to independence

Alternate location for Atlantic-Pacific canal

Became commonwealth of U.S. in 1898

Two countries occupied by U.S. Marine police force during Wilson's presidency

Presidential Programs

In the blank provided, write the program or term described. Then put that answer in the chart under the correct president.

1. put nearly one hundred million acres under federal control _Reclamation Act_
2. reform which lowered tariff and resulted in the first income tax _Underwood Tariff Act_
3. American investments used to influence foreign affairs _"dollar diplomacy"_
4. compromise between Russia and Japan which ended their war _Treaty of Portsmouth_
5. fair treatment and equal opportunity for all motto _"Square Deal"_
6. The "Great White Fleet" was an example of this. _"battleship diplomacy"_
7. He should have been hand-picked for this court position rather than the presidency.
   chief justice
8. This made the United States a policeman over Latin America. _Roosevelt Corollary_
9. He clashed with the president over public land use. _Gifford Pinchot_
10. Under this motto, there would be strong regulation, not trust-busting.
    "New Nationalism"
11. This act balanced private banking and state-controlled banking. _Federal Reserve Act_
12. a five-man board to define and halt unfair labor practices _Federal Trade Commission_
13. built as a link between Atlantic and Pacific shipping _Panama Canal_
14. labor's "Magna Carta" _Clayton Antitrust Act_
15. dealt with Pacific territorial claims and the Open Door policy
    Root-Takahira Agreement

ROOSEVELT	TAFT	WILSON
Reclamation Act	"dollar diplomacy"	Underwood Tariff Act
Treaty of Portsmouth	chief justice	Federal Reserve Act
"Square Deal"	Gifford Pinchot	Federal Trade Commission
"battleship diplomacy"		Clayton Antitrust Act
Roosevelt Corollary		
"New Nationalism"		
Panama Canal		
Root-Takahira Agreement		

Fundamentalists vs. Progressives

Chart the conflicting views of fundamentalists and progressives on the following issues.

Issue	Fundamentalists	Progressives
Government	Limited government with limited powers	Increased powers of government
Nature of Man	Man is sinful by nature.	Man is basically good.
Improvement of Mankind	Kingdom of God is established on earth.	Natural progression by evolution
Problem Solving Methods	Through forgiveness and cleansing by God through the death and resurrection of Jesus Christ	False solutions through education, improved living conditions, and more political and economic opportunities
Leadership	D. L. Moody Benjamin B. Warfield Evangelists such as Billy Sunday	Walter Rauschenbusch John Dewey

SKILL: Charts

Diary of a Soldier

The following entries are from *Letters and Diary of Alan Seeger*, the diary of an eighteen-year-old American, Alan Seeger, who joined the French army within the first months of World War I—three years before American troops would be involved. Read the entries and then answer the questions.

Toulouse, Sunday, September 27, 1914.—Fifth Sunday since enlistment. Beautiful sunny afternoon. Peace. The stir of the leaves; noise of poultry in the yards near by; distant church bells, warm southern sunlight flooding the wide cornfields and vineyards. Everything is ready for departure today.

To his mother, Toulouse, September 28, 1914.—We are still held up here, though all preparations for departure have been made and everyone expected to be off yesterday. We are entirely equipped down to our three days' ration and 120 rounds of cartridges. The suspense is exciting, for no one has any idea where we shall be sent.

Sunday, October 11, 1914.—This morning comes the unexpected news of the fall of Antwerp. This is the most important event of the war to date. It means the entire subjugation of Belgium. The Germans, as far as I can see, occupy all the territory they have coveted and all that they would keep in the event of their ultimate victory. It is my idea that they will now wage a defensive war entirely, limiting themselves to holding what they have. The impending winter will wonderfully favor them in this plan of campaign. The strong defensive lines they have reared on their front will enable them to detach large forces to cope with the Russians. On the whole, their situation seems good and the task of the French and English in driving them back a desperately hard one.

To his mother, Aube, October 17, 1914.—After two weeks here and less than two months from enlistment we are actually going at last to the firing line. . . . Imagine how thrilling it will be tomorrow and the following days, marching toward the front with the noise of battle growing continually louder before us. The whole regiment is going, four battalions, about 4,000 men. You have no idea how beautiful it is to see the troops undulating along the road in front of one.

Vertus, October 20, 1914.—Made a short morning's walk of 16 kilometers,—still through the great battle-field. The Germans retreated along the road we marched over. Extraordinary evidences of the artillery fire. Pine woods with the branches all ripped to pieces; large sized trees broken clean off in the middle. Today we passed through the villages of Marsain and Bergeres. The first was completely destroyed, not a house on

the main street had escaped the fire. Nothing but blackened walls and here and there the inhabitants standing with sullen faces in their ruined doorways. The scene of the marching column down the ruined street,—a scene that will become familiar to us,—was imposing.

November 10, 1914.—Fifth day of our second period in the trenches. Five days and nights of pure misery. We came up here Thursday evening a foggy, moonlit night, bright enough to show the fields through which we ascended, spattered with shell-holes as thick as molehills, and the pine woods full of shattered trunks and broken branches. . . . Our position this time has been a claypit on a high summit above the chateau. Owing to its exposed and dangerous character very formidable bomb proofs have been built at this point of the line. To these we have been confined for five days from morning to night. A big hole here in the pit, a few yards from our door, marks the place where three men of Battaillon D were killed by a shell only a few days before our arrival. . . . It is a miserable life to be condemned to, shivering in these wretched holes, in the cold and the dirt and semidarkness. It is impossible to cross the open spaces in daylight, so that we can only get food by going to the kitchens before dawn and after sundown. The increasing cold will make this kind of existence almost insupportable, with its accompaniments of vermin and dysentery. Could we only attack or be attacked! I would hear the order with delight. The real courage of the soldier is not in facing the balls, but the fatigue and discomfort and misery. What a winter's prospect if our campaigning is only going to be alternate between these two phases of inaction and discomfort!

On the Aisne, April 28, 1915.—Patrouille! [Patrol!] How the heart beats to hear the word go round in the afternoon and to learn that one has been chosen to take part in it. To escape from the eternal confinement of the trenches, to stalk out into the perilous zone between the lines and there, where death may lurk in every thicket and uncertainty encompasses one close as the night, to court danger for several hours under a fine starlit sky, this is the one breath of true romance that we get in the monotonous routine of trench warfare. . . .

We went out, fifteen men, a few nights ago to reconnoitre a new ditch that had appeared on the face of the hillside high up under the German lines. . . . There were fruit trees all about this part of the hillside. They were clouded with bloom, reminding one of Japanese prints. But another odor as we advanced mingled with that of the blossoms, an odor that, congealed all through the winter, is becoming more and more intense and pervasive as the warm weather increases. Among the breaths of April, fragrant of love and the rebirth of life, it intrudes, the sickening antithesis—the odor of carrion and of death. . . .

Single or in heaps or files they lie—in attitudes of heroism or fear, of anguish or of pity—some shielding their heads with their sacks from the hail of shrapnel, many with the little "first aid" package of bandages in their hands, with which they have tried to stanch their wounds. Frenchmen and Germans alike, rigid bundles of soaked cloth, filling the thickets, sodden into the muddy beet fields, bare and exposed around the trenches on the bleak upper slope and amid sacks, broken guns and all the litter of the battle-field. The sight is one which may well be unnerving the first time, but one soon gets used to it, and comes to look upon these images of death with no more emotion than on the empty cartridge cases around them which, indeed, in a way they do resemble. Having served their purpose the material shell remains, while their vitality has been dispersed into the universe to enter into new combinations in that eternal conservation of energy which is the scientist's faith and that imperishability of anything that is beautiful in the human personality, which is the poet's.

After spending another year and three months in entrenched warfare, Alan Seeger's dream would come true. He was in the first battalion to participate in the attack upon Belloy-en-Santerre on July 2, 1916. The following excerpt is from a reporter's account of the battle.

The Legion attacks Belloy-en-Santerre. With a rush, it starts, its two leading companies pressing straight forward, beneath the crash of bursting shells, across a chaos of detonations. . . . Three hundred metres yet to cross and they will reach the enemy. . . . En avant! [Forward!]

But suddenly, hands relax their grasp, arms open, bodies stagger and fall, as the clatter of the German mitrailleuses [machine guns] spreads death over the plain where, but a moment before, men were passing.

Epilogue
One of the first to fall was Alan Seeger. Mortally wounded, it was his fate to see his comrades pass him in their splendid charge and to forego the supreme moment of victory to which he had looked forward through so many months of bitterest hardship and trial. . . . So it was not until the next day that his body was found and buried, with scores of his comrades, on the battle-field of Belloy-en-Santerre.

Answer the following questions on a separate sheet of paper. Answers will vary. Use this for discussion.

1. What was Alan's feeling about the war? Was he in the war for personal gain? How did he feel about trench warfare? Students may use words from the diary describing Alan's emotions.

2. Was Alan's opinion of the Germans' motive for war correct? What did the Germans actually desire? How did he view the French and English task? Students may use the October 11 diary entry and what they know of the actual course of the war.

3. What evidences did the troops see of battle? How did the villagers appear to feel about the war and combatants? Students should use the October 20 entry and following entries.

4. Why was patrol duty looked forward to? What did the men encounter? At the end of the April 28 entry, to what does "poet's" refer? What does this paragraph reveal about Alan's philosophy of life? Looked forward to it as a change from inactivity. Dead bodies. Refers to the poet's faith. Discuss verses such as Job 10:9; Job 34:15; and II Cor. 5:8 which refer to the state of the soul and body at death. Discuss pantheism or New Age philosophies and their fallacies.

5. Was Alan Seeger a hero? Let the students define the term and then go to the Bible for God's perspective. The teacher may want to ask if Alan would have been a hero to himself, his parents, other Americans, the French, or God. Discuss heroes of the Bible and present-day heroes.

Poster Propaganda

Analyze the four war posters on page 453 of the text. Answer the questions for each poster in the box relative to the poster's position on the page. Students' answers will vary.

---

1. How does the poster make you feel?
   Answers will vary. _____
   _____
   _____
   _____

2. Why do you think the poster would make people want to buy bonds?
   Answers will vary. _____
   _____
   _____
   _____

3. How has the artist aroused the desired emotions? By showing immigrants to whom liberty was extended, the artist has reminded many citizens of their past and of how much they owe to America.

---

1. How does the poster make you feel?
   Answers will vary. _____
   _____
   _____
   _____

2. What is the message of the poster?
   The message is that waste will hurt the soldiers and their families.
   _____

3. How has the artist aroused the desired emotions? The artist's use of a dark pencil drawing helps make the soldier look cold, tired, and hungry. The soldier is looking directly at the viewer as if to ask for support.

---

1. How does the poster make you feel?
   Answers will vary. _____
   _____
   _____
   _____

2. Why was the slogan "Remember Belgium" used? Belgium was a country that Germany ruthlessly overran with total disregard for its neutrality.
   _____
   _____

3. How has the artist aroused the desired emotions? The artist has used the dark silhouettes of a German dragging a young girl against the background of a burning city to play on some of our worst fears.

---

1. How does the poster make you feel?
   Answers will vary. _____
   _____
   _____

2. Who is the woman supposed to be?
   Liberty or the United States

3. What does the slogan "Every Garden a Munition Plant" mean? It means that each garden is a resource to help renew a soldier's depleted energy. A healthy soldier means a stronger army.
   _____

4. How does the artist convey the message? By portraying the planter as the beautiful Lady Liberty, the artist encourages all women to do their patriotic duty.

REINFORCEMENT: Section II   SKILL: Analysis   99

Map Study: The World at War

Refer to the map on page 456 of the text and a historical world atlas to complete the map below.

1. Label these countries with abbreviations: Germany (Ger.), Sweden (Swe.), France (Fr.), Denmark (Den.), Great Britain (G.B.), Belgium (Bel.), Netherlands (Neth.), Norway (Nor.), Spain (Sp.), Portugal (Por.), Italy (It.), Greece (Gr.), Bulgaria (Bul.), Serbia (Serb.), Austria-Hungary (Aus.-Hun.), Switzerland (Swi.), Russian Empire (Rus. Emp.), Ottoman Empire (Otto. Emp.).

2. Label the Argonne Forest, the Marne River, the Belleau Wood, and Château-Thierry.

3. Using a green pencil, color the Allied countries.

4. Using a red pencil, color the Central Power countries.

5. Using a blue pencil, color in the neutral nations.

6. Using a yellow pencil, draw in the line of the front in 1918.

7. Using a purple pencil, draw in the armistice line.

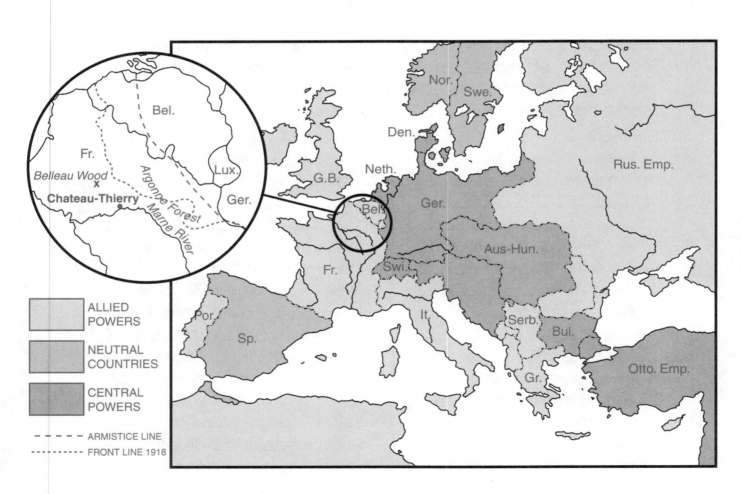

SKILL: Maps

Weapons of War

Several new and improved forms of weaponry were used in World War I. Use an encyclopedia or other reference to fill in the following chart. Students' answers will vary depending on the resource they use.

Weapon	Definition	Inventor	Battle Use	Effectiveness
Big Bertha	21-centimeter gun which attained a range of 76 miles	Germany	used for bombarding entrenched enemy and for creeping barrage	effective because of its long distance capabilities and explosive power
tank	heavily armored vehicle designed to be an all-terrain vehicle	Britain	used to cross trenches and destroy bunkers containing machine guns	succeeded in offensive maneuvers but needed more armor against big guns
airplane	one- or two-seater, single- or double-winged flying machine fitted with machine guns	developed in several countries—One was the British Vickers, another was the German Fokker.	initially used in reconnaissance—later used in air-to-air combat	effectively bombed enemy lines but was a slow, easy target
submarine	a double-hulled, torpedo-shaped vessel capable of undersea propulsion	several invented around the same time—German U-boat best known	used to sink enemy craft with torpedoes and deck guns—later armed with anti-aircraft guns	effectively destroyed many vessels carrying men and munitions
chemical warfare	the use of chemicals such as chlorine and phosgene dispersed from cylinders	used first by the Germans	used in trench warfare to injure or kill entrenched enemies	caused mostly injuries—After nerve gas, most countries banned its use.
hand grenade	hand-thrown missile with priming and bursting charges inside	developed originally in the 17th and 18th centuries—British Mills Bomb is best known.	two types used in trench warfare — One injured with shrapnel, the other relied on explosion.	highly effective in taking enemy bunkers or clearing enemy trench positions
dirigibles	hydrogen-filled balloons with an attached cabin which could carry bombs	Graf Ferdinand von Zeppelin designed the German version.	used for stealthy approach far into enemy territory where reconnaissance or bombing missions took place	very effective in bringing the war to the home front of the enemy—used to bomb cities

What's the Question?

Here are the answers. Put the questions in the blanks provided.

1. another way of talking about food saving and production _What was "Hooverizing"?_

2. a general association of nations for the purpose of affording mutual guarantees of political independence and territorial integrity to great and small states alike
   What was the League of Nations?

3. General John J. Pershing _Who was the general sent to capture Pancho Villa?_

4. German-Americans and Irish-Americans _Who were the hyphenates?_

5. They dominated the Versailles conference and were called the "Big Four." _Who were_
   President Woodrow Wilson, Georges Clemenceau, Vittorio Orlando, and David Lloyd George?

6. April 6, 1917 _What was the date on which America declared war on Germany?_

7. It was the ship that marked the violation of America's right to open sea travel.
   What was the Lusitania?

8. the name given to President Wilson's statement that another attack on a passenger or merchant vessel would break ties with Germany and perhaps lead to war
   What was the Sussex pledge?

9. It allowed a national draft to increase recruitment. _What did the Selective Service Act_
   accomplish?

10. "Es ist nichts, es ist nichts." _What were Archduke Franz Ferdinand's last words?_

11. Kaiser Wilhelm II _Who was the leader of the German people during World War I?_

12. unofficial anthem of the American doughboy _What was "Over There"?_

13. It was the battle that turned the tide of the war. _What was the Argonne offensive?_

14. Pancho Villa _Who led a Mexican uprising against America?_

15. It was a German policy which said that all ships in the war zone would be sunk.
    What was unrestricted submarine warfare?

16. It was the event that sparked World War I. _What was the murder of Archduke Franz Ferdinand?_

17. November 11, 1918 _What was the date of the armistice?_

18. Intercepted and decoded by the British, it called for Mexican support of the German cause.
    What was the Zimmerman telegram?

19. He was America's "Ace of Aces." _Who was Eddie Rickenbacker?_

20. Under these, it became a crime to criticize the war effort. _What were the Espionage and_
    Sedition Acts?

21. Wilson's plan for peace _What were the Fourteen Points?_

22. January 28, 1919 _When was the Treaty of Versailles signed?_

Cartoon Capers

Many a truth is said in jest. This was the way that J. Ding got the truth to the people in 1928 with the following cartoon. Look at the cartoon and answer the following questions.

1. Who was Al Smith? <u>New York governor who ran in the 1928 presidential election against Herbert Hoover</u>

2. What does he say he wants to do for the farmer? <u>He says he wants to help.</u>

3. Does he look ready to help the farmer? <u>no</u>

4. What does he look ready to do? <u>He looks ready to play golf.</u>

5. Who is his wife? <u>the Democratic party</u>

6. Does she look ready to work? <u>perhaps a little</u>

7. What does she have with her? <u>a milk pail and a milking stool</u>

8. What do they reveal about her? <u>The stool shows that she will work, but the size of the pail suggests that she will not work too hard.</u>

9. Briefly tell what Tammany Hall was. (See Chapter 15 of the text.) <u>Tammany Hall was the controlling political organization in New York City during the last half of the nineteenth century. It continued to influence politics into the early 1900s.</u>

10. What is Ding implying by having Tammany in the picture? <u>that Tammany Hall support was behind Al Smith, lending support to his misrepresentation</u>

11. What does the dog represent? <u>farm interests trying to protect the farmer and his property</u>

12. Do you think he can win against the tiger? (Explain) <u>No, the tiger has more power than the dog.</u>

13. Why does the farmer look perplexed? <u>Perhaps he wonders what this man can do for him.</u>

14. In your own words, tell what you think this cartoon would have meant to people who saw it on June 4, 1928. <u>Answers will vary. The students should realize that the farm groups would have seen the threat of a candidate backed by big city political power. The students should also see that the hard-working, perhaps conservative, farm groups would have disapproved of the liquor and leisure represented here in the Democratic party.</u>

ENRICHMENT: Section I   SKILL: Analysis   103

Who's Who?

Using the text, put the following terms in the chart under the correct president.

hands-off approach	heart attack	"normalcy"
Teapot Dome scandal	engineer	Al Smith
into office by presidential death	World War I	Ohio Gang
secretary of commerce	depression	Albert B. Fall
governor of Massachusetts	Vermont	food relief
"The business of America is business."	newspaper editor	looked presidential
first Republican president of 1920s	Harry Daugherty	Charles G. Dawes

Warren G. Harding	Calvin Coolidge	Herbert Hoover
Teapot Dome scandal	hands-off approach	secretary of commerce
first Republican president of 1920s	into office by presidential death	engineer
looked presidential	governor of Massachusetts	depression
newspaper editor	"The business of America is business."	World War I
Harry Daugherty	Vermont	Al Smith
"normalcy"	Charles G. Dawes	food relief
Ohio Gang		
Albert B. Fall		
heart attack		

SKILLS: Charts and Using Resources

Positive or Negative Influence?

Write a brief description of each of the following 1920s personalities and describe their positive or negative influence on 1920s society.

1. **Charles A. Lindbergh, Jr.:** First person to fly solo nonstop across the Atlantic Ocean from New York to Paris. He was considered a hero by the United States and Western Europe. Lindbergh's flight showed the world the potential of air power. He was a positive influence in the 1920s.

2. **Al Capone:** A notorious criminal who controlled a crime ring in Chicago that made money through the illegal manufacture, transportation, and sale of alcoholic beverages. He was an evil influence through violence and crime.

3. **William J. Bryan:** Bryan was a dominant 1920s personality. He ran for president and was Secretary of State, a political crusader, and a reformer. Bryan defended Christianity at the Scopes trial. He brought a positive conservatism to government through the positions he held and the causes he supported.

4. **Albert Einstein:** Einstein was a German scientist whose theory of relativity was used by writers and philosophers to encourage doubt of the Scriptures and moral standards. The theory took away the idea of absolutes in science. Einstein's theory influenced society in a negative way by leading to the suggestion that Scripture is not absolute truth. Some used this idea to justify their rejection of moral restraints and responsibilities.

Scripture Search

Read the following excerpt from the 1929 book *The American Omen* by Garet Garrett. Use the questions below to analyze the philosophy of finance evidenced in the book and manifested by many Americans before the stock market crash of 1929.

People may ruin themselves by saving instead of spending. . . . It is now true for the first time in the economic annals of the race because the problem of production has been solved. How to produce enough, even more than enough, is no longer any problem at all. We continue to recommend thrift as a private and public virtue without realizing that when once you have solved the problem of production, then thrift universally and rigorously practiced—the kind of thrift that means doing with less in order to save more—is economically disastrous. . . .

We must mind that we spend enough—to keep our existing industrial machine going at ideal capacity, for unless we demand and consume what it is ready to provide, there will be unemployment, from unemployment underconsumption, and the rhythm of prosperity will break. . . .

Increasingly the anxiety of modern business is how to stimulate effective wanting, how to induce people in the average to exert themselves more in order to be able to have and consume more. Installment selling has that motive. Give a man on credit a better house in a better neighborhood, give him on credit a garage and a motor car to put in it, give him on credit all the goods that belong to a higher standard of living than he has hitherto thought himself able to afford, and what will he do? Will he give up these things because he cannot afford them? Not for that reason. Not for any reason whatever if he can help it. He will think of ways to increase his income. This means only that he will exert himself more to produce other things the equivalent of these, and that will be more than he ever produced before. From *THE AMERICAN OMEN* by Garet Garrett, copyright 1928 by E. P. Dutton, renewed. Used by permission of Dutton, a division of Penguin Putnam Inc.

1. In your own words, briefly summarize what the selection is saying. (1) Saving is no longer needed because production is up. (2) We need to spend money to maintain demand so that there will be employment. (3) Installment buying will cause people to find a way to make more money.

2. Read Proverbs 6:6-11. Does this passage agree or disagree with the philosophy in this article? Explain your answer. disagrees—The students should see the necessity for circumspect living, being aware of the quick changes that can and do occur in financial affairs.

3. Now read Luke 12:16-34. Does this passage agree or disagree with the philosophy in this article? Explain your answer. Answers will vary. The students should see the problems with putting their trust in savings rather than in the Lord and with saving merely for the purpose of accumulating goods. The teacher may want to discuss the purpose of money.

4. Based on these two Scripture passages, what balance needs to be achieved in financial matters? The students should see the need for balance in spending and saving. They should see this in light of God's command to stewardship. They should also consider where treasures are to be laid up.

5. Read Proverbs 22:7. How does this apply to installment buying? The students should recognize the burden of responsibility that occurs when money is owed. The students should discuss how indebtedness affects relationships between loan maker and debtor and how indebtedness affects the use of money for God's work.

Make It Right!

In the following paragraphs, several words or phrases have been numbered. As you read the page, decide if those numbered items are correct or incorrect. If they are incorrect, cross them out and write the correct word or phrase above them.

After the war, the nation wanted to get back to business as usual, and [1] ~~isolationism~~ *normalcy* was the goal of all the people. Many things in the nation had changed with the needs of war. American farms had been feeding Americans and [2] Europeans. After the war, when the young men went back to the farm, they found that food prices had [3] plunged due to the [4] ~~meager~~ *bountiful* harvest of 1920. When they went to the city, they found war industries [5] closed. These factors combined to take unemployment to a high of [6] ~~18.3~~ *11.9* percent.

The nation faced not only economic changes but also the emotional impact of war. Americans were warily looking for other enemies. They feared the [7] ~~agnostics~~ *anarchists* who had talked about overthrowing the United States government. This fear caused a temporary panic called the [8] Red Scare. It also helped reinforce the idea that it was time for America to take care of things at home. [9] ~~Internal~~ *Foreign* policy of the 1920s was [10] isolationism. However, America was now a world power, and with that power came responsibility for keeping the peace. The [11] ~~Dawes Plan~~ *Washington Naval Conference* limited [12] ~~air force~~ *navy* capabilities by establishing a ratio of power among the five most powerful countries. Another interesting plan was the [13] Kellogg-Briand Pact, which declared war to be [14] ~~inhumane~~ *illegal*. Closer to home, effort was made to improve relationships with [15] ~~Canada~~ *Latin America*.

With war behind them, Americans now had to get to the business of everyday life. Evolution, [16] Freudian psychology, and the [17] theory of ~~actuality~~ *relativity* (time and space vary according to the location and motion of the observer) were causing people to question Scripture and longstanding moral values. The questioning even went into the mainline religions, resulting in major denominational splits. The fundamentalists left the Northern Baptist Convention and formed the [18] General Association of ~~Rural~~ *Regular* Baptists. As the fundamentalists tried to hold the faith, one area their efforts centered on was the teaching of evolution in public schools. [19] ~~John T. Scopes~~ *Clarence Darrow* was the defense attorney in the Scopes trial and used [20] William Jennings Bryan as an expert witness for the Bible. The evolutionists lost the case, but the antievolutionists lost the publicity battle.

The 1920s were a time of material prosperity and spiritual depravity. What seemed like such a good time to many was about to come to an abrupt halt.

Twenties Tangle

Answer the questions. Unscramble the circled letters to form a phrase that describes the era in the chapter.

1. The first commercial radio station came on the air with the call letters K D K A
   in P I T T S B U R (G) H .

2. (R) U D O L P H   V A L E N T I N O was the heart-throb of many silent-movie fans of the early 1920s.

3. Suspicion of foreigners contributed to the passage of the N A T I O N A L
   O R I G I N S   A C (T) .

4. The day the bottom fell out of the stock market is called B L A C K
   (T) H U R S D A Y .

5. The first "million-dollar gate" for sports involved boxer J A C K
   D E M P (S) E Y .

6. "The Lone Eagle" and "Lucky Lindy" were nicknames for C H A R L E S
   L I N D B (E) R G H .

7. The "Saint Valentine's Day Massacre" involved A L   C A P O (N) E 's gang.

8. Fear of foreigners and blacks brought back the Reconstruction organization called the
   K U K L U X   K L (A) N .

9. The term B U L L   M A (R) K E T is used to describe a stock market that is characterized by rising prices and optimism.

10. The " F L A M (I) N G   Y O U T H " of the 1920s caught the attention of the world with their disregard for moral standards and their rebellious behavior.

11. Henry Ford's original car design was replaced by the M (O) D E L   A in 1927.

12. Shoppers of the 1920s found that they could buy now and pay later with an
    I N S T A L L M E (N) T   P L A N .

13. Babe Ruth became known as the " S U L T A N   O F   S (W) A T ."

14. Girls who flaunted their freedoms with short skirts, short hair, and boyish looks were called
    F L A P P (E) R S .

15. Buying low and selling high is known as S P E C U L A T (I) O N .

The

R O A R I N G   T W E N T I E S

Deep Depression

Only the very rich were able to weather the Great Depression with little discomfort. The average family found itself living from job to job and paycheck to paycheck, never knowing how long either would last. It is remarkable to look back and see how many things families did without and yet led a fairly normal existence. A partial list could include toothpaste (baking soda was substituted), cars, refrigerators or iceboxes, gas stoves, snacks, toilet paper (magazines or catalogs were used), toys, and other entertainment.

Everything that was used was taken care of or reused in a different function. Towels and sheets became washrags or dust cloths. Thin-soled shoes had cardboard or newspaper laid inside them. Seed sacks became towels or even dresses and curtains.

Industrious people looked for odd jobs to make ends meet between jobs or paychecks. Growing extra food in gardens, washing windows, doing yard or garden work, painting, and running errands all became moneymaking opportunities.

Suppose a plunge in the stock market took place tomorrow and the United States was once again faced with a depression. In the spaces below, make a list (in order of importance) of items you could do without. Keep only the necessities! Students' answers will vary.

1. excess clothing
2. video games
3. VCR
4. air conditioner
5. radio
6. tape player
7. pets
8. outside entertainment
9. television
10. snack foods, soda
11. insurance
12. car(s)
13. extra personal items
14. hair dryer, curling iron
15. clothes dryer
16. hose or socks

Make a list of jobs that you could do to help your family make ends meet. Remember that these jobs must be things that people will need to have done even in times of depression.

1. baby-sitting
2. lawn keeping
3. housecleaning
4. running errands
5. redeeming aluminum cans
6. washing cars

Name three things that could be reused and ways that you would reuse them.

Item	Reuse
1. string from a package	shoelaces
2. balloon	cut for rubber bands
3. old tire	soles for sneakers

The ABCs of Economic Recovery

Give the names of the following 1930s programs and organizations. Write a brief description of the purpose of each. Which president initiated each?

1. POUR— President's Organization for Unemployment Relief–took the place of PECE but never had the resources to deal effectively with the growing crisis–Hoover

2. PECE— President's Emergency Committee for Employment–coordinated the efforts of public and private charities; funneled relief information to government–not enough resources–Hoover

3. NCC— National Credit Corporation–nation's prosperous banks to help establish credit reserve fund to assist banks in danger of failing–banks were unwilling to risk money–Hoover

4. RFC— Reconstruction Finance Corporation–was given $500 million to loan to businesses (mainly banks) to stabilize banking industry–did not inspire credit expansion or return confidence–Hoover

5. CCC— Civilian Conservation Corps–put young, unmarried men to work in reforestation and soil conservation projects–popular and lasted until after U.S. entered World War II–FDR

6. AAA— Agricultural Adjustment Act–established method of subsidizing farm products and aided debt-ridden farmers in danger of farm foreclosure–program criticized–FDR

7. NRA— National Recovery Administration–designed to carry out the activities prescribed by NIRA–unsuccessful and eliminated–FDR

8. TVA— Tennessee Valley Authority–extensive project to build dams along the Tennessee River to provide flood control and cheap electricity–FDR

9. PWA— Public Works Administration–work relief provider that built schools, courthouses, hospitals, bridges, and other public facilities–lasted six years–FDR

10. WPA— Works Progress Administration–created to eliminate relief roles–employed almost anyone in almost any job–failed to eliminate unemployment–FDR

11. FERA— Federal Emergency Relief Administration–carried on some CWA programs and created others–not enough to eliminate the dole–FDR

12. CWA— Civil Works Administration–put jobless to work building roads, playgrounds, and airports–FDR

13. FDIC— Federal Deposit Insurance Corporation–devised to insure the bank deposits of millions of Americans against loss–FDR

14. CIO— Congress of Industrial Organizations–union made up of unskilled industrial workers who had suffered hardships and who wanted more from their jobs–later joined AFL–FDR

15. AFL— American Federation of Labor–union limited to skilled craftsmen–later united with CIO–FDR

16. NIRA— National Industrial Recovery Act–tried to organize voluntary guidelines for industries to increase employment, maintain wages, and reduce unwanted competition–FDR

Dust Bowl Disaster

Many times in his effort to make a living with the least expense to himself, man has not taken the time to consider the long-term effects of his methods. At the beginning of the twentieth century, settlers poured into the Great Plains hoping to benefit from the fertile soil there. Unfortunately, they did not plan for the effect that their plowing would have on the region's ability to hold its topsoil.

In Genesis 1:26, God gave man dominion (control) over all the earth and told him to subdue it (bring it into bondage). In Genesis 2:15, He put man in the garden "to dress it and to keep it." The word for "keep" in that verse is also translated "watch" or "preserve." In this case, it implies having charge of. The earth is the Lord's, but He has put it into man's care. With this principle in mind, answer the following questions. Students' answers will vary.

1. What events led to the "Dust Bowl" of the 1930s? The increase in farmed acres due to the influx of settlers into the Great Plains caused more acres to be stripped of their prairie grass. When drought came, there were no natural grasses to hold the topsoil.

2. What measures could have been taken to prevent the "Dust Bowl"? Fewer settlers could have been allowed into the new territory. More prairie sod could have been left in strips between plowed fields. Rows of trees could have been planted as windbreaks.

3. Give an example of a current ecological problem. Answers include trash, chemical waste, nuclear waste, acid rain, and ozone depletion.

4. What caused this problem? Answers will vary.

5. How could the problem have been prevented or its effect been reduced? Answers will vary.

6. In India, the main religion prevents people from eating "sacred cows," yet many people there go hungry. Do you think this action agrees with Scripture? Support your conclusion with Scripture. God told Noah in Genesis 9:3 that every living thing was food for him just as the plants were given as food before the Flood. The people who refuse to eat are worshiping the cows in their religion and in that way are practicing idolatry, which is forbidden in Exodus 20:3-5.

Optional Discussion

Do you think the United States has a right to refuse to send Third World countries aid because they are cutting down the rain forests?

Forget Your Troubles

In the midst of troubles, people look for diversions to take their minds off the current situation. Answer the following questions about popular depression-era diversions. Then fit the answers into the chart under the appropriate category.

1. Futuristic scientific inventions, such as his "two-way wrist radio," made him popular with adults and children alike. _Dick Tracy_

2. She started out as a child star and in adult life became an ambassador. Shirley Temple

3. This infamous duo shocked the nation with their bloody spree of theft and murder. Bonnie and Clyde

4. Orson Welles's version of this story sent the unsuspecting nation into a panic over the invasion of aliens. _War of the Worlds_

5. In an attempt to be the first woman to fly around the world, she disappeared in the Pacific. Amelia Earhart

6. The nation listened as this giant craft exploded. the _Hindenburg_

7. This epic Civil War story, first introduced as a book, was dramatized at the end of the decade. _Gone with the Wind_

8. He introduced "swing" and was followed by a host of others. Benny Goodman

9. This was the first feature-length cartoon. _Snow White_

10. Bruno Hauptmann was eventually convicted of this crime. Lindbergh baby kidnapping

11. This little girl challenged the depression with courage and pluck. _Little Orphan Annie_

12. Thousands of girls swooned to this man's crooning. Bing Crosby

13. This man topped the most wanted list. John Dillinger

14. The serial adventures of this cowboy hero started with the William Tell Overture and "Hi-ho, Silver! Away!" the _Lone Ranger_

15. Dinosaurs and cave men appeared together in this Stone Age story. _Alley Oop_

Real-life Drama	Comic Strips	The Big Screen	Radio
Bonnie and Clyde	_Dick Tracy_	Shirley Temple	_War of the Worlds_
Amelia Earhart	_Little Orphan Annie_	_Gone with the Wind_	Benny Goodman
the _Hindenburg_	_Alley Oop_	_Snow White_	Bing Crosby
Lindbergh baby kidnapping			the _Lone Ranger_
John Dillinger			

SKILLS: Charts and Comprehension

A Time of Tyrants

Never before had the world seen tyrants in such cooperation, each with his own ultimate plan and goal but willing to use the others for a time to get closer to that goal. Use your book and an encyclopedia to answer the following questions about each leader. Answers will vary in completeness according to the students' sources.

Germany

1. Leader's name _Adolf Hitler_
2. What was he called? _the Führer_
3. What was his father's profession and economic status? _customs official; poor_
4. How did he come to power? _Through the Nationalist party, he was able to gain recognition and eventually ran for president in 1930. Three years after his defeat, the president invited him to be chancellor of Germany. Hitler became Supreme Commander on the death of President Hindenburg._
5. How long did he lead? _from 1933 to 1945_
6. What was his party's name? _the Nazi party_
7. Give a brief summary of his effect on the German people. _Hitler's amazing ability to move an audience brought the German people behind him as they strove to establish the German people as the perfect race. Through his leadership, they gained much territory at the loss of hundreds of thousands of lives. In the end, the German nation was defeated and demoralized._
8. What was his party's symbol? _the swastika, an ancient Aryan symbol for luck_
9. When he was young, what career did this man want to pursue? _He wanted to be an artist._

Italy

1. Leader's name _Benito Mussolini_
2. What was he called? _Il Duce_
3. What was his father's profession and economic status? _blacksmith; poor_
4. How did he come to power? _He came into popularity by his speaking. When a general strike was called in 1922, the fascists marched on Rome and took over the government. Shortly thereafter Mussolini was made prime minister._
5. How long did he lead? _from 1922 to 1943_
6. What was his party's name? _the Fascist party_
7. What was his first profession? _Mussolini was a journalist._
8. Give a brief summary of his effect on the Italian nation. _Initially, Mussolini was able to revive the country through social reform and public works. His power-hungry behavior eventually turned the party against him, and they plotted his downfall. By this time, Mussolini's popularity had waned, and his achievements were forgotten in the defeat of war._
9. What was his party's symbol? _the fasces, a bundle of rods bound around an ax_

Soviet Union

1. Leader's name. _Joseph (Dzhugashvili) Stalin_

2. What did his name mean? _came from the Russian word "stal" which means steel_

3. What was his father's profession and economic status? _cobbler (shoemaker); poor_

4. How did he come to power? _Stalin moved up through the ranks of the Bolshevik party until he_ _became the party's Central Committee chairman. This position opened the way for his dictatorship._ _When Lenin died in 1924, Stalin took over._

5. How long did he lead? _from 1924 until his death in 1953_

6. What was his party's name? _the Communist party_

7. Give a brief summary of his effect on the Soviet nation. _He initiated state-organized_ _industrialization. Millions of peasant farmers were forced to combine their property into collective_ _farms. Those who wouldn't cooperate were put into concentration camps. Stalin was responsible_ _for tens of millions of deaths during his time in power._

8. In an effort to increase his political power, this leader had millions executed in what are now called _purges_ .

9. What was his party's symbol? _the hammer and sickle_

Optional Essay
Using the information above and an encyclopedia, answer the following essay questions.

1. As you can see from the background information, all three of these leaders came from a working-class background. How do you think this affected their political decisions? How do you think it affected the nations' reception of them?

   Answers will vary. The students may infer that the working class may have been more likely to desire _revolutionary forms of government. The students should also note that, generally, a leader is better_ _received when the people believe he can understand their social and economic situation._

   _____

   _____

   _____

   _____

2. Of the three governments represented by these leaders, which two are most alike? Why are they different from the third? Explain.

   Fascism and Nazism are most alike in that they allowed a capitalistic economic structure in which _individuals are allowed to retain their property. In contrast, the Communist government enforced a_ _socialistic economic structure in which all property became the government's to use as the party saw_ _fit._

   _____

   _____

   _____

   _____

SKILL: Using Resources

Map Study: The European Theater

Refer to the map on page 516 of the text as well as an encyclopedia or a historical atlas to complete the map.

1. Label the following:

    Countries—Algeria (Alg.), Austria (Aus.), Belgium (Bel.), Czechoslovakia (Cz.), Denmark (Den.), Egypt (Eg.), France (Fr.), Germany (Ger.), Italy (It.), Libya (Lib.), Morocco (Mor.), Norway (Nor.), Poland (Pol.), Soviet Union (USSR), Tunisia (Tun.), United Kingdom (U.K.)

    Cities—(Use the dots to locate.) Algiers, Berlin, Casablanca, Dunkirk, Leningrad, London, Moscow, Munich, Oran, Paris, Potsdam, Rome, Stalingrad, St. Lô, Tripoli, Warsaw

    Regions—Rhineland, Sudetenland

    Rivers—Rhine, Rhone

2. Color the following:

    Yellow—Neutral nations in 1942

    Red—Axis or Axis-controlled countries

    Black line—the Maginot Line

    Green—Allied or Allied-controlled countries

3. Locate and label:

    ✹ —the Battle of Britain

    🗡 —Vidkun Quisling's treachery

    ⚡ —first blitzkrieg

    🔥 —Operation Torch's three landing sites

    OH—Operation Husky's objective

    D-day—Operation Overlord site

    ➡ —General Patton's advance after D-day

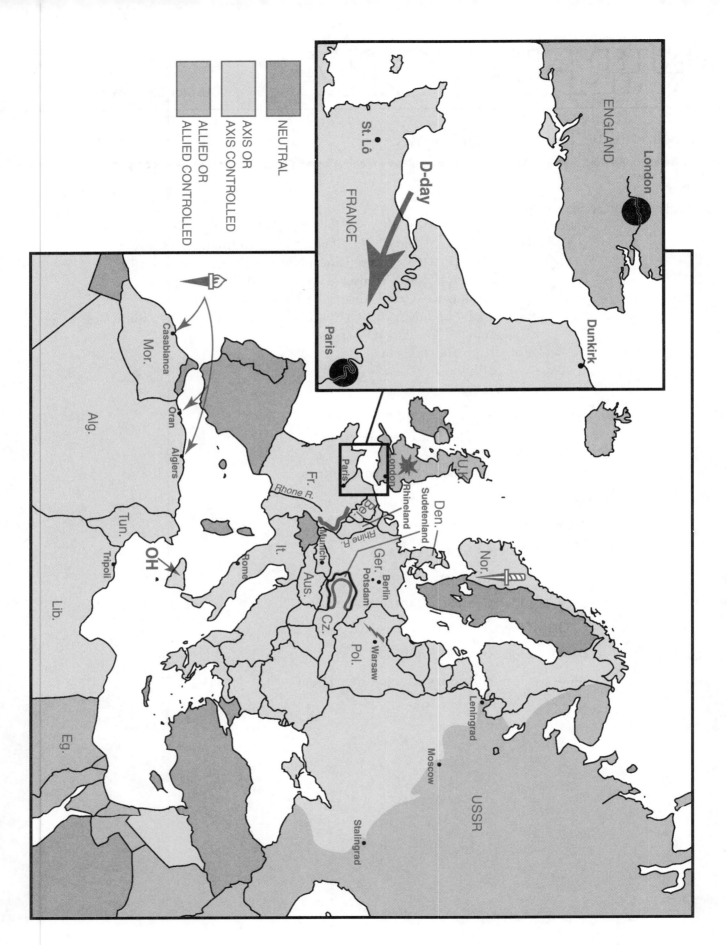

LEGEND

NEUTRAL

AXIS OR
AXIS CONTROLLED

ALLIED OR
ALLIED CONTROLLED

London
ENGLAND

Dunkirk

D-day

St. Lô

FRANCE

Paris

Casablanca
Mor.
Oran
Alg.
Algiers
Tun.
Tripoli
Lib.
Eg.

Paris
Fr.
Rhone R.
It.
Rome
Munich
Aus.
Cz.
Bel.
Rhine R.
Rhineland
Sudetenland
Ger.
Berlin
Potsdam
Warsaw
Pol.
U.K.
Den.
Nor.

Leningrad
Moscow
USSR
Stalingrad

OH

Map Study: The Pacific Theater

Refer to the map on page 528 of the text as well as an encyclopedia or a historical atlas to complete the map.

1. Label the following:

   Countries—Australia, China, Dutch East Indies, French Indochina, Malaya, New Guinea

   Islands—Aleutian, Guadalcanal, Guam, Hawaii, the Marianas, Marshall, Midway, Solomon, the Philippines

   Places—Bataan Peninsula, Coral Sea, Manila, Tokyo

2. Draw a line showing the farthest extent of Japanese expansion in the Pacific.

3. Fill in the blank and label the map.

   a. What two Japanese cities were struck with a nuclear bomb? _____Hiroshima_____
   and _____Nagasaki_____ Label each city on the map with a nuclear cloud.

   b. What location was bombed by the Japanese, bringing the United States into World War II? _____Pearl Harbor_____ Label the location with a bomb.

   c. What location was the site of the largest sea battle in history? _____Leyte Gulf_____
   Label the location with a torpedo.

   d. What tiny island was the site of a battle where "uncommon valor was a common virtue"? _____Iwo Jima_____ Label that island with a medal.

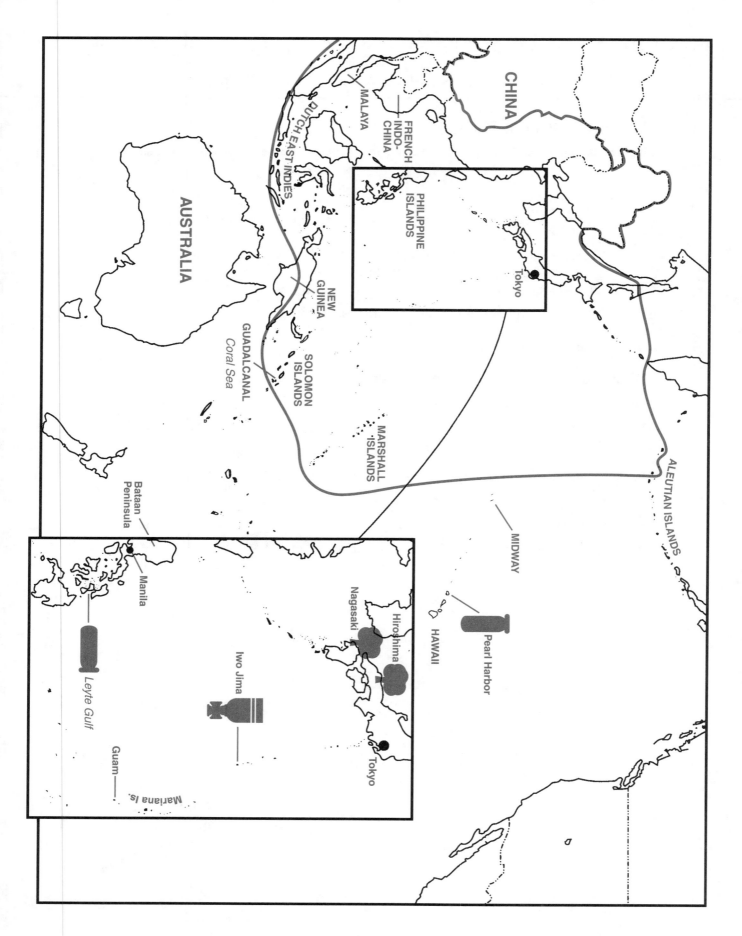

CHINA

MALAYA

FRENCH
INDO-
CHINA

DUTCH EAST INDIES

PHILIPPINE
ISLANDS

Tokyo

AUSTRALIA

NEW
GUINEA

GUADALCANAL

Coral Sea

SOLOMON
ISLANDS

MARSHALL
ISLANDS

ALEUTIAN ISLANDS

MIDWAY

Bataan
Peninsula

Manila

Nagasaki

Hiroshima

HAWAII

Pearl Harbor

Iwo Jima

Leyte Gulf

Guam

Mariana Is.

Tokyo

Who, What, When, Where

Answer the following questions.

1. What was the German term for the "lightning war"? _blitzkrieg_____

2. Who said "Your boys are not going to be sent into any foreign wars"? _FDR_____

3. Where was the Atlantic Charter drawn? _off the coast of Newfoundland on the ships___
   Augusta and _Prince of Wales_____

4. When did the Japanese attack Pearl Harbor? _December 7, 1941_____

5. Who said "I shall return"? _Douglas MacArthur_____ To whom did he say it?
   _Philippine people_____

6. Besides Okinawa, where did the U.S. want a foothold to Japan? _Iwo Jima_____

7. What was the French Maginot Line? _a series of forts on the west side of the Rhine River_____
   _____ What was its German counterpart? _Siegfried Line_____

8. Who agreed to let Hitler take western Poland? _Stalin_____ What was
   their agreement called? _Nazi-Soviet nonaggression pact_____

9. Where did the Germans aim their attack in the operation code-named "Barbarossa"?
   _at three Russian cities — Leningrad, Moscow, and Stalingrad_____

10. What were three reasons that the United States stayed out of war so long?
    _(1) traditional isolationist policy (2) nonpayment of war debts (3) the Great Depression___

11. Who were the Nisei? _second-generation Japanese-Americans_____ What happened
    to them in America during World War II? _They were put in detention camps._____

12. Who symbolized the American women in industry during the war? _"Rosie the Riveter"___

13. What was a blue star banner? _a banner hung in the window to show how many sons were___
    _fighting in the war_____ What was a gold star banner? _a banner hung in___
    _the window to show how many sons had died in war_____

14. Where did Operation Overlord start? _on the Normandy coast_____

15. Who was the Supreme Allied Commander in 1944? _General Dwight Eisenhower_____

16. When was D-day? _June 6,1944_____

17. Who was the "Desert Fox"? _Erwin Rommel_____ What forces did he command
    and where? _the Afrika Korps in North Africa_____

18. What was a "cricket"? Who used it? When? _The "cricket" was a small, clicking noisemaker___
    _used by paratroopers dropped inside Normandy on D-day._____

19. Where did the "bulge" occur in the Battle of the Bulge? _fifty miles into the Allied line___
    _to Bastogne_____

20. Who massacred millions from racial and ethnic groups, and what was that massacre
    called? _Hitler massacred millions in the Holocaust._____

21. When was the bomb dropped on Hiroshima? _August 6, 1945_
22. When was the bomb dropped on Nagasaki? _August 9, 1945_
23. What was the turning point of the Japanese offensive? _the Battle of Midway_
24. Who took over the presidency upon FDR's death? _Harry Truman_
25. What was the name of the plane that dropped the first bomb? _Enola Gay_
26. What was the German word for their armed forces? _Wehrmacht_
27. What was the German word for their air force? _Luftwaffe_
28. Where was the "great arsenal of democracy"? _the United States of America_
29. What is *Anschluss*? _"union" between Germany and Austria_
30. In Norway, whose name is synonymous with *traitor*? _Vidkun Quisling_
31. What committees did the pacifists and isolationists organize? _America First Committees_
32. When did the Yalta meeting of the Big Three take place? _February 1945_
33. Who were the Big Three? _Roosevelt, Churchill, and Stalin_
34. What issue did the Russian leader at Yalta agree to but not practice? _the support of democratic elections and governments in all liberated nations_
35. Who were *kamikazes*? _suicide pilots used by the Japanese air force to attack American ships_

36. When did Hitler write a book? _when he was in prison_
37. What was it called? _Mein Kampf_
38. Who headed the U.S. Army, and who headed the U.S. Navy on the Pacific front? _General Douglas MacArthur and Admiral Chester A. Nimitz_
39. What occurred on a national scale in 1943 to help improve the government's tax flow? _payroll deductions of income taxes_
40. Where did the "death march" occur in World War II? _the Bataan Peninsula in the Philippines_
41. Who were the two new faces at Potsdam? _Harry Truman and Clement Attlee_
42. What was the one item upon which they agreed? _the demand for Japan's unconditional surrender_
43. Where did Operation Torch take place? _in North Africa_
44. Who commanded that mission? _General Dwight Eisenhower_
45. When did the War Production Board begin? _January 1942_
46. What was its function? _to conserve materials for war production_
47. What was the most significant Pacific conquest of summer 1944? _the taking of the Marianas_ What effect did it have on the future fight? _gave the Allies a base for bombing Japan and the Philippines_
48. What act set aside $7 billion to supply embattled nations? _Lend-Lease Act_
49. Who gave a speech about four freedoms? _FDR_ What were his "Four Freedoms"? _freedom of speech and worship and freedom from want and fear_

SKILL: Test-taking

To Win or Not to Win

General Douglas MacArthur and President Truman had a falling out after MacArthur made statements that were critical of the administration's decisions in the Korean War. After his dismissal, MacArthur spoke to a joint session of Congress and made the statement, "In war, indeed, there can be no substitute for victory." Evaluate that statement in light of the following questions.

1. Read Luke 14:28-32. According to that passage, is MacArthur's statement correct? Explain. <u>The student should see that a good leader sometimes makes concessions when</u> <u>defeat is inevitable or victory is too costly.</u>

    What principle is this passage teaching? <u>The scriptural principle here is "counting the cost."</u>

2. At the end of World War I and World War II, what do you think was the overall attitude of the civilians and veterans toward what had been accomplished? Do you think it was the same after the Korean and Vietnam Wars? If it was different, what made the difference? Does this support or weaken General MacArthur's statement? Explain.

    <u>The students should sense that the attitude after the World Wars was positive. The United States</u> <u>came away victorious. After the Korean and Vietnam Wars, the nation was disillusioned. The difference</u> <u>came from the fact that although many died in the World Wars, the aggressors were crushed, and the</u> <u>task was accomplished. Victory gave their death significance. In Korea and Vietnam, thousands died,</u> <u>the enemy was still free to threaten, and the original task was left unfinished. The students should see</u> <u>that the emotional effect of victory does appear to support MacArthur's statement.</u>

3. Did the Korean War effectively contain the threat of communism in Asia? Explain.

    <u>The students should recognize that the immediate threat was resolved and that the boundary had</u> <u>been retained, but the long-term threat remained. Communism was deterred in Korea but would rise</u> <u>up as a threat to Vietnam.</u>

4. What possible differences would there have been in world affairs if the United States had won a decisive victory in Korea? Explain. <u>Answers will vary. All answers are supposition.</u>

    <u>The students may say that victory would have further strengthened the United States's position as</u> <u>defender of democracy. Pursuing victory could also have drawn the United States into world war</u> <u>on a nuclear scale. It could also have preserved democracy in Asia for this century, or it could have</u> <u>ended in defeat and humiliation for the United States.</u>

Map Study: The Korean War

Refer to a world atlas and/or an encyclopedia to complete the map.

1. Locate and label the following:

    Countries—China, Manchuria, North Korea, South Korea
    Places—Seoul, Inchon, Yalu River, Panmunjom

2. Label the following:

    Boundaries—38th Parallel, 1953 Armistice Line, the line showing the farthest
    advance of U.N. forces into North Korea

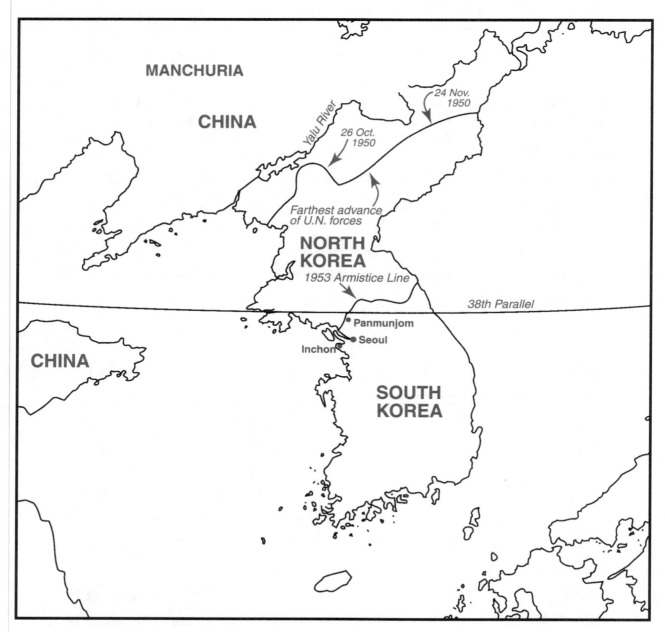

Advertising Anomalies

With televisions in many homes, the 1950s saw the onset of advertising on an unprecedented scale. Today, many consumers buy products based on the brand name, the packaging, the jingle, the endorsements, or how the product will enhance their image. Christians need to be good stewards of God's money and buy a product based on its worth. In the following exercise, analyze three different brands of the same food product. Answer the questions about each brand and draw your conclusion at the end. Answers will vary depending on the students' choices. The teacher may want to do this in class in groups or in one demonstration at the front of the class.

What is the product's brand name? _____

Do you know anything about this product from advertising? If so, what did the advertising say about the product? _____

_____

How does its packaging appeal to you? (color, type style, picture, shape) _____

_____

_____

What are this product's ingredients? _____

_____

On a scale of 1 to 5, 5 being highest, how would you rate this product's taste? _____

What was the cost of this product per ounce? _____

What is the product's brand name? _____

Do you know anything about this product from advertising? If so, what did the advertising say about the product? _____

_____

How does its packaging appeal to you? (color, type style, picture, shape) _____

_____

_____

What are this product's ingredients? _____

_____

On a scale of 1 to 5, 5 being highest, how would you rate this product's taste? _____

What was the cost of this product per ounce? _____

What is the product's brand name? _____

Do you know anything about this product from advertising? If so, what did the advertising say about the product? _____

_____

How does its packaging appeal to you? (color, type style, picture, shape)

_____

_____

What are this product's ingredients? _____

_____

On a scale of 1 to 5, 5 being highest, how would you rate this product's taste? _____

What was the cost of this product per ounce? _____

Analysis

Which product would you have bought prior to analysis? _____

What would your motivation for purchase have been? _____

Which product is most expensive? _____

How do you think advertising affected the cost of this product? _____

_____

Which product, if any, tastes best? _____

Which product, if any, is most visually appealing? _____

Based on calories, fat grams, and nutritional content, which product, if any, is most nutritious?

_____

Based on all the information you have gathered, which product is the best buy for your money? (Defend your decision.) __The students should defend their decisions using all the

 information gained. If they decide on a more expensive product, they should tell why the product

 is worth the extra cost._____

_____

_____

_____

Optional Discussion The teacher could suggest a certain item such as athletic shoes.
What makes a brand of clothing popular? Is it more comfortable than comparable non-brand items? How do you determine if an item is popular? Why does popularity change the price of an item? What do brand names say about you if you wear them?

"Red and Yellow, Black and White"

In 1908, the British author Israel Zangwill produced a play in which one of the characters said, "America is God's great melting pot where all the races of Europe are melting and re-forming!" Since that time, immigrants have poured into America from every nation in the world, bringing an ethnic diversity that sometimes doesn't melt away. This diversity is often the cause of misunderstanding, conflict, and sometimes violence. In the 1960s, the conflict came to the attention of the American people in the form of the civil rights movement, but even now it continues to breed controversy. The Bible has much to say about how we react to others. Study the Scripture verses below and answer the questions on the next page.

1. Write a two- or three-sentence summary of how God deals with diverse people and cultures in each of the following Scripture passages.

   • I Samuel 16:7
      Physical appearance or other things that seem to make people qualified in men's eyes are not used by God as a determiner. The Lord looks on the heart to judge people.

   • Matthew 7:15-20
      God judges a person by his fruits, and we should too.

   • Romans 10:1-13
      There is no difference between the Jew and the Greek (Gentile). Salvation is free to all.

   • I Corinthians 3:10-15
      God judges Christians on the basis of their works to determine their rewards but not their salvation.

   • 1 Corinthians 12:1-27
      God brings the body of believers together and uses their gifts and abilities with no mention of race or culture.

   • James 2:1-9
      God warns us not to pay special attention to rich people. God says that "respecting persons" is a sin.

2. Based on these passages, do you think culture or race affects a person's ability to be saved? Support your answer with Scripture. <u>Romans 10:12-13 shows that God opened</u> <u>salvation to all.</u>

3. Once you are saved, how does God judge you? Support your answer with Scripture. <u>According to I Corinthians 3:13-15, God judges the saved by their works.</u>

4. Look up the word *prejudice* in a dictionary and write a general definition. <u>an adverse</u> <u>judgment or opinion formed beforehand or without knowledge or examination of the facts</u>

5. Write at least five groups that people are prejudiced against. Include more than just racial groups. <u>Students' answers will vary but will probably include ethnic groups (African-Americans, Hispanics, etc.), economic groups (very rich, very poor, etc.), social groups (elderly, women, handicapped, etc.), and religious groups (Amish, fundamentalists, etc.).</u>

6. Do you think that a prejudice about a group of people affects a person's willingness to witness or minister to that group? Explain why or why not. Which most affects your witness? <u>The student will probably note that prejudice does affect our ministering or witnessing to a group of people. They may attribute the hindrance to fear, hatred, disgust, feelings of superiority, and so on. Answers will vary.</u>

Optional Activity—Have the class discuss one of the following scenarios. Choose two leaders who will then take turns choosing team members until the class is divided in half.

Topic #1
Should a person who has tested HIV positive be allowed to enroll in your school?

Topic #2
You come late to camp, and you need a room. You see that there are two rooms with only one person in them. In one room is the richest kid in the youth group; in the other room is this kid who rides the bus from the worst part of town to come to church every Sunday. You do not know either kid well. With whom should you room?

Topic #3
A couple has been waiting to adopt a baby for eight years. The adoption agency calls and says they have a baby for them. When they arrive, they find that the baby has a severely deformed leg but, other than that, is beautiful. Should they adopt the child?

Postwar Events

Put the letter for the correct date next to the event.

____A____ 1. Truman becomes president of the United States

____F____ 2. South Korea is invaded by North Korea

____M____ 3. Fidel Castro overthrows the Cuban dictator

____P____ 4. construction of Berlin Wall begins

____N____ 5. John F. Kennedy takes the oath of office

____R____ 6. civil rights march on Washington, D.C.

____G____ 7. McCarthyism

____Q____ 8. Cuban Missile Crisis

____O____ 9. Bay of Pigs

____C____ 10. Iron Curtain descends on Eastern Europe

____E____ 11. Berlin Airlift forces the end of the Soviet blockade

____H____ 12. H-bomb developed

____J____ 13. truce between North and South Korea begins

____K____ 14. "one nation under God" is added to Pledge of Allegiance

____B____ 15. United Nations begins

____I____ 16. Dwight D. Eisenhower takes the presidential oath

____D____ 17. NATO is formed

____L____ 18. Warsaw Pact is established

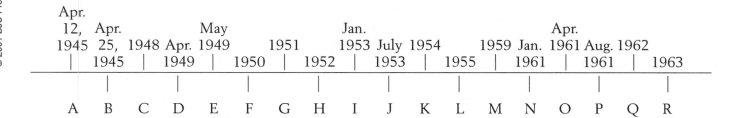

Who Am I?

Read each statement and decide who would have said it. Write his or her name in the blank.

_____Jackie Robinson_____ 1. I was the gifted black athlete who accepted the challenge to integrate professional baseball.

_____Alger Hiss_____ 2. I was a former State Department official who was accused of passing secret documents to a Soviet spy.

_____Mao Zedong_____ 3. Under my leadership, the Communist Chinese gained control of mainland China.

_____Thomas Dewey_____ 4. The *Chicago Daily Tribune* printed what everyone expected when it mistakenly headlined that I had defeated Truman.

_____John F. Kennedy_____ 5. I started the Peace Corps as part of my New Frontier legislative program.

_____Fidel Castro_____ 6. I created a Communist state just ninety miles from the Florida coast.

_____Billy Graham_____ 7. I gained worldwide fame after a tent meeting in Los Angeles.

_____Orval Faubus_____ 8. In Little Rock, Arkansas, I used the National Guard to block nine black students from going to the local high school.

_____William F. Buckley_____ 9. I founded the *National Review,* a magazine that promotes conservative views.

_____Soviet Premier Khrushchev_____ 10. The Berlin Wall was constructed under my leadership.

_____Chiang Kai-shek_____ 11. I led the Nationalist Chinese and headed that government in exile in Taiwan.

_____Harry Truman_____ 12. I expanded the New Deal and called my legislative program the Fair Deal.

_____Joseph McCarthy_____ 13. I headed a Senate subcommittee to investigate whether or not Communists were present in our government.

_____Julius & Ethel Rosenberg_____ 14. We helped give classified information about the atomic bomb to the Soviets.

_____Dwight Eisenhower_____ 15. With my vice president, Richard Nixon, I won the 1952 election by a landslide.

_____Martin Luther King, Jr._____ 16. Influenced by Mahatma Gandhi and Henry David Thoreau, I supported using nonviolent resistance and civil disobedience in the civil rights movement.

_____Benjamin Spock_____ 17. My child-care book popularized the theories of Freud and Dewey and was outsold only by the Bible.

_____Rosa Parks_____ 18. I refused to give my bus seat to a white man. My arrest led to a bus boycott in Montgomery, Alabama.

_____Henry A. Wallace_____ 19. After the president fired me, I ran against him on the Progressive ticket in the 1948 election.

The Johnson Years—Salving Society's Ills

Answer the following questions about pages 564-67 of the text.

1. What was the goal of Johnson's "Great Society"? _to create a government that could help all_ _citizens to better themselves politically, socially, and economically_

2. What was the first and most important of Johnson's civil rights bills? _the Civil Rights_ _Act of 1964_

    A. List four racial injustices it hoped to end. _unfair voter registration, racial discrimination in_ _public buildings, segregation in public schools, and racial discrimination in projects and_ _institutions_

    B. What did the bill create to ensure nondiscrimination in hiring practices? _the Equal_ _Opportunity Commission_

3. In the next year, what act would help give black Americans more political power? _the_ _Voting Rights Act of 1965_

4. What department did Johnson use to attack poverty? _the Office of Economic Opportunity_ _(OEO)_

5. In what three ways did the government attack poverty? _through job training and_ _placement, through Head Start, and through VISTA_

6. What allowed Johnson to push eighty-nine bills through the legislature in 1965? _the_ _overwhelming Democratic majority in Congress._

7. Which one of those bills would have the widest impact on the nation? _Medicare_

8. What was the policy of the Supreme Court in the 1960s called? _judicial activism_

9. Name the five civil rights cases for which the Warren Court is best known. After the case name, write in your own words what happened as a result of each case.

    A. _Brown v. Board of Education—It brought about the beginning of the end of segregated schools._

    B. _Gideon v. Wainwright—It required that poor defendants receive proper legal representation. It_ _must be provided by the state if the defendant cannot afford it._

    C. _Miranda v. Arizona—It required that criminals be informed of their rights before they are_ _questioned._

    D. _Engel v. Vitale—The Supreme Court ruled that prayer in the public school was a violation of the_ _separation of church and state._

    E. _Roth v. United States—The Supreme Court took First Amendment protection away from_ _obscenity but then defined it so narrowly that the pornography business boomed._

Map Study: War in Vietnam

Refer to the map on page 569 of the text to complete this activity.

1. Label the following locations.

> Countries—North Vietnam, South Vietnam, China, Burma, Laos, Thailand, Cambodia
>
> Places—Gulf of Tonkin, Gulf of Siam, Hanoi, Haiphong, Saigon, Mekong Delta, Phnom Penh

2. Draw the Ho Chi Minh Trail and the DMZ on the map.

3. Answer the following questions.

Why was it called the Tet Offensive? <u>It was launched during the celebration of Tet.</u>

What was napalm? <u>a defoliant used on jungle trees so that no one could take cover under them</u>

Who were the Viet Cong? <u>pro-Communist South Vietnamese</u>

What occurred as a result of the incident in the Gulf of Tonkin? <u>President Johnson</u>
<u>asked for a joint resolution of Congress that resulted in the escalation of American involvement</u>
<u>in Vietnam.</u>

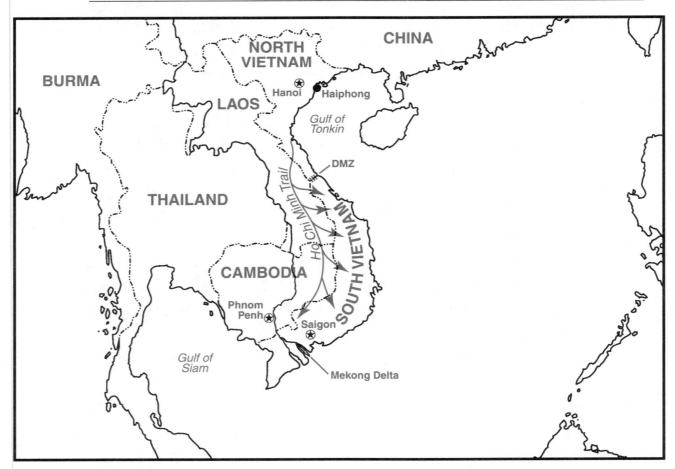

SKILL: Maps

The Bible as a Guidebook

We know that man is inherently sinful and, therefore, incapable of producing a perfect society. Yet we also know that God says He will bless those who keep His ways (Prov. 8:32). In this exercise you are to give scriptural ways of dealing with social problems. Phrase your answers as if you were speaking to the group listed. Students' answers will vary. References are given as aids.

1. The problem of hiring discrimination or pay discrimination against minorities

   • To the person discriminating _Deuteronomy 24:14; I Samuel 16:7; Matthew 7:15-20_ _____

   _____

   _____

   _____

   _____

   • To the person being discriminated against _Matthew 5:10-12; I Peter 2:21-25; I Peter 3:16-18_

   _____

   _____

   _____

   _____

   _____

2. The problem of poverty

   • To the financially comfortable _Exodus 22:25; Leviticus 23:22; Deuteronomy 15:7;_ ____

   I Samuel 2:7; Proverbs 14:21, 31; Proverbs 19:17; Proverbs 21:13 _____

   _____

   _____

   _____

   _____

   • To the poor _Psalm 40:17; Proverbs 19:1; Philippians 4:11; I Timothy 6:6, 8; Hebrews 13:5_

   _____

   _____

   _____

   _____

   _____

3. The care of the elderly
   - To the young The story of Ruth; Exodus 20:12; Deuteronomy 5:16; Matthew 15:4; Matthew 19:19; Romans 13:7; II Timothy 5:3-4, 16

   - To the elderly Exodus 20:5; 34:7; Numbers 36:8; Psalm 78:2-4; Proverbs 9:14; 17:6; II Corinthians 12:14; I Timothy 5:8

4. The problem of civil disobedience
   - To those using it for change Mark 12:17; Luke 20:25; Romans 13:1-7; I Thessalonians 5:15

   - To the Christian Romans 13:1-7; Philippians 2:4-8; II Timothy 2:24; Titus 3:1

SKILL: Bible Study

Space Race Matching

Match each of the phrases with the person, thing, or event it describes. Some letters will not be used, and some will be used more than once.

__F__	1.	He spent thirty-four hours in orbit.
__U__	2.	Germany's rocket pioneer
__K__	3.	code name for project designed to lift man into orbit
__E__	4.	had two hatches to allow for space walks
__I__	5.	president who initially committed U.S. resources to the space program
__C__	6.	lunar module name
__L__	7.	Goddard's nickname
__R__	8.	world's first satellite
__O__	9.	fuel for Goddard's early rockets
__S__	10.	von Braun bomb development used to blitz London
__E__	11.	project designed to put two men into orbit
__T__	12.	His flight landed less than four miles off target.
__M__	13.	the first man on the moon
__V__	14	number of feet the first rocket flew
__J__	15.	He helped finance Goddard's experiments.
__P__	16.	father of American rocketry
__H__	17.	first American to orbit in space
__A__	18.	*Eagle* was part of this space project.
__D__	19.	first American to walk in space
__B__	20.	command module name

A. Apollo
B. *Columbia*
C. *Eagle*
D. Edward White
E. Gemini
F. Gordon Cooper
G. gunpowder and alcohol
H. John Glenn Jr.
I. Kennedy
J. Lindbergh
K. Mercury
L. "Moony"
M. Neil Armstrong
N. Nixon
O. oxygen and gasoline
P. Robert H. Goddard
Q. "Spacey"
R. *Sputnik 1*
S. V-2
T. Walter Schirra
U. Werner von Braun
V. 184 feet
W. 236 feet
X. 1926
Y. 1935

What Ever Happened to . . . ?

Using an encyclopedia or the Internet, locate information on America's seven original astronauts. Find out briefly where their space careers led them. Answers will vary.

1. Walter M. Schirra, Jr.— Only astronaut to fly in Mercury, Gemini, and Apollo space programs. Retired from the navy and NASA in 1969. Served as an officer and director of several companies and formed his own consultant company, Schirra Enterprises. Lives with his wife in California.

2. Donald K. Slayton— Scheduled to pilot second orbital mission, but was replaced because of heart fluttering. Changed lifestyle and heart flutterings ceased. Trained at cosmonaut center near Moscow for Apollo-Soyuz test project. His only flight was in 1975. Retired from NASA in 1982; became a consultant and authored books on the U.S. space program. Died in 1993 of brain cancer.

3. John H. Glenn, Jr.— In 1962 was the first American to orbit the earth. Resigned from NASA in 1964 and retired from marines in 1965. Worked as a consultant to NASA and as an executive. Became a U.S. senator from Ohio in 1974, serving four consecutive terms. In 1998 became the oldest astronaut to fly in space at age 77, retired from Senate in 1999, and resides with his wife, Anne.

4. Scott Carpenter— In 1962 went into space with his main goal to prepare for lunar landings. In 1965 participated in U.S. Navy's SEALAB II as an aquanaut. Retired from Navy in 1969. Has been engineering consultant, wasp breeder, and novelist. Lives with his wife, Maria.

5. Alan B. Shepard, Jr.— In 1961 became the first American in space. In 1969 became part of Apollo 14 crew and was the fifth man to set foot on the moon. Retired from the navy and resigned from NASA in 1974. Founded his own business and named it for his two missions, Seven Fourteen Enterprises. Died in 1998 from a lengthy illness.

6. Virgil I. "Gus" Grissom— First man to fly in space twice. In 1966 was to command the first Apollo Earth orbit mission, but along with astronauts White and Chaffe died when a fire engulfed their Apollo I capsule during a launch pad test.

7. L. Gordon Cooper— First flight was in 1963, the last Mercury mission. Was the first American astronaut to sleep in orbit and first to make a second orbital flight. Resigned from NASA and the air force. From 1974 to 1980 worked as vice-president in research and development for Disney Enterprises. Now president of a firm that develops aviation fuel.

SKILL: Using Resources

A Woman's Place

There is much controversy over the place of women in society today. On one hand, there are those who say that a woman should be able to pursue anything she chooses with no extra burdens of home responsibilities. On the other hand, there are those who say that a woman should never work outside the home. The Scriptures should be the ultimate guide for making decisions; therefore, it is imperative to know the principles found in God's Word. Answer the questions below and then use the Bible and a concordance to write your philosophy concerning a woman's place in society. It may be useful to discuss the Christian woman's role in society with your parents, pastor, youth pastor, Bible teacher, or other respected Christians.

This activity could effectively be used as a discussion topic for the whole class. Guide your students into profitable discussion, realizing that mothers in both categories will be represented by your class. Answers will vary throughout the exercise.

1. List at least three reasons women give for not working outside the home. They want to rear their children. They have enough work in the home. They can minister better to others in the church when their days are free.

2. List at least three complications in a woman's life that can result from not working outside the home. no money to put older children in Christian school or college, a sense of guilt for not using skills developed in college, a feeling of losing touch with the "outside" world

3. List three benefits which can come to a woman's life and family from her not working outside the home. She will have more time to comparison shop, thus saving money. She will be able to train her children more in their early years. She will be free to use her talents at church.

4. What are three jobs that women can do in their homes to help financially? baby-sitting, ironing, sewing, mailing, many freelance jobs (any three)

5. How can a husband and/or children be supportive of a woman's decision not to work outside the home? They can be proud of what she accomplishes at home. They can be content with their financial situation. They can provide her opportunities to use her talents outside the home.

6. On a separate sheet of paper, make a chart comparing the advantages and disadvantages of working in the home, especially dealing with time, money, and emotional, social, physical, and spiritual considerations.

7. List at least five improvements in technology in the past fifty years that have reduced a woman's workload at home. clothes dryer, washing machine, dishwasher, self-cleaning oven, self-defrosting refrigerator, vacuum cleaner, no-wax flooring, wall-to-wall carpeting

© 2001 BJU Press. Reproduction prohibited.

8. List at least three reasons women give for working outside the home. finances, bored at home, want to use college education, want some independence, to put kids in Christian school

9. List three complications in a woman's life that can result from working outside the home. lack of time for getting home chores done, fatigue, difficulty finding baby sitters or after-school care, no relaxation time, home and job conflicts

10. List three benefits that working outside the home can bring to a woman's life and family. can allow children to go to Christian school, can allow family finances for recreation or vacation, can help woman feel she is using her talents, can help family to pull together to make schedules work

11. How can a husband and/or children help a woman balance home chores and outside work? The family can help by taking more responsibility for running the home (e.g., taking turns with meal preparation and clean-up, running errands, giving quiet time if necessary for extra time on job-related activities).

12. On a separate sheet of paper, make a chart comparing the advantages and disadvantages of working outside the home, especially dealing with time, money, and emotional, social, physical, and spiritual considerations.

13. According to the Scriptures, what are some of a woman's responsibilities in marriage? honor her husband; love her husband and children; be discreet, pure, a keeper at home, good, obedient to her husband, adorned with a meek and quiet spirit, industrious, economical; and take care of her family's needs

14. Does a woman's role change as her life progresses? Explain. (Consider marriage, birth of children, death of or divorce from a spouse, and marriage of children.) Most students will answer yes. They should note that household duties don't always need as much time, so the woman may have more time in which to pursue a career. They should also note that the death of or divorce from a spouse often puts the whole burden of support on the woman, and outside work becomes difficult to avoid.

15. In Proverbs 31:10-31, find at least five character traits that mark God's example of a virtuous woman. trustworthy, supportive (of her husband), industrious, works willingly, frugal, wise, decisive, strong, compassionate, diligent, organized, kind

16. On a separate sheet of paper, write your philosophy (belief) of what a woman's place in society should be. Support it with Scripture. Titus 2:3-5 and I Peter 3:1-12 are good places to begin. The students' answers will vary, but they should show that they have looked at all areas of the situation and have searched the Bible for guidance.

Three Men and the Presidency

Place the following information into the chart below the president it describes.

unelected president	Panama Canal Treaty	golfing accident
peanut farmer	final defeat in Vietnam	George McGovern
pardoned former president	Camp David Accords	football player
oil embargo	Ayatollah Khomeini	granted amnesty
defense of human rights	ended gold standard	Watergate affair
House minority leader	SALT II Treaty	veto
John C. Calhoun	resignation	Spiro Agnew
"born-again" claim	high unemployment rate	Daniel Ellsberg
outsider to Washington	sweaters and jeans	12%-13% inflation
Iranian hostages	hostile Congress	

NIXON	FORD	CARTER
oil embargo	unelected president	peanut farmer
John C. Calhoun	pardoned former president	defense of human rights
ended gold standard	House minority leader	"born-again" claim
resignation	final defeat in Vietnam	12%-13% inflation
George McGovern	high unemployment rate	Panama Canal Treaty
Watergate affair	football player	Camp David Accords
Daniel Ellsberg	veto	Ayatollah Khomeini
Spiro Agnew	golfing accident	SALT II Treaty
	hostile Congress	outsider to Washington
		Iranian hostages
		granted amnesty
		sweaters and jeans

The Christian and Politics

The New Right included a large portion of conservative Christians who began to voice their views in the political arena. Answer the following questions about the effect of Christianity on government.

1. Refer to pages 82, 235, 482, 611-13, and 643-44 of the text. Next to each religious movement, list its social or political effect.

   a. First Great Awakening

   a. As a national movement, it helped unite the colonies. It reaffirmed the equality of all men and brought power to the people, not only in churches but also in government.

   b. Second Great Awakening

   b. Revival fueled the drive for moral reform. Many leaders of the abolition and prohibition movements were converts of the revival.

   c. Fundamentalist Rise

   c. It attempted to hold down the irreligious mood in America. It also fought the teaching of evolution in the public schools.

   d. Religious Right

   d. They helped to stop the ERA and tried to affect other moral issues such as legalization of abortion, drug abuse, and homosexuality.

2. Why do you think that political reform is often the result of religious reform? _____
   Answers will vary. The students should see that spiritual revival usually changes the way a person votes, and the voting power of a group influences those in office to change their decisions.

3. Can we ever expect the world's political system to reach perfection? Why or why not?
   No. Students should understand that the natural man is bent to sin. Even if all the world were saved, there would still be sin and imperfections in the system. Until the world is ruled by the sinless one, the world will continue in its course of sin and decline.

4. Should the Christian be involved in politics? _____ Explain your answer with Scripture. Answers will vary. If the student's answer is yes, possible Scripture would be Matthew 5:13-16 with the explanation that we are to be light and salt in the earth. If his answer is no, possible Scripture could be Matthew 28:19-20 with the explanation that we have a commission from God that should not be hindered by more temporal concerns.

5. What can you do to make an impact on politics now? Answers will vary. Pray for revival in America. Pray for our political leaders. Be vocal about your religious viewpoints. Write letters of concern to your local political leaders on issues that affect your religious freedoms. Vote as soon as you are old enough so that you can exercise your political freedom.

A Decade of Political Disaster

The 1970s were filled with domestic and foreign disaster for the American people. Answer the following questions.

1. What other presidents that you have studied were plagued by scandals in their administrations? _Ulysses S. Grant, Warren G. Harding_____

2. What character trait did Ford have that Nixon hoped would help his administration?
   _Ford was known for his honesty, something that Nixon was lacking in._____

3. What single event devastated Ford's early popularity? _He pardoned Nixon for any_____
   _wrongdoing in the Watergate affair._____

4. Why was Congress so determined to maintain control during Ford's administration?
   _They didn't want the excesses of the Nixon administration repeated._____

5. What does OPEC stand for? _Organization of Petroleum Exporting Countries_____

6. Why did OPEC call for an oil embargo? _to retaliate against the United States for supporting_
   _Israel when Israel was attacked by Egypt and Syria_____

7. What caused gasoline to be scarce during the early days of the embargo? _Nixon had_____
   _wage and price controls in place that held gasoline at a low price._____

8. Why did the prices skyrocket later? _The prices skyrocketed when price controls were lifted._
   _As with anything, low supply and high demand cause higher prices._____

9. How did environmental concerns contribute to the energy crisis? _To reduce pollution,_____
   companies changed from coal to oil as a power source and strained resources more.

10. Define *stagflation*. _a condition in which high prices and wage inflation couple with stagnant_
    _consumer demand and high unemployment_____

11. What were three causes of stagflation? _The energy crisis, the budget deficit, and abandoning_
    the gold standard fueled inflation without making a way to reduce unemployment.

12. What occurred in 1971 that seemed to make it necessary for Nixon to end the gold
    standard? _The United States suffered its first trade deficit since the 1890s._____

13. When the gold standard was dropped, what happened to the value of the dollar?
    _It began to drop in value in relation to foreign currency._____

14. What three things contributed to Gerald Ford's loss in the 1976 election? _the high_____
    _unemployment rate, the pardon of Nixon, and perception of Ford as a bumbler_____

15. What decision caused Carter to lose the approval of veterans? _Carter's decision to_____
    _grant amnesty to draft dodgers_____

16. What was central to Carter's foreign policy? the defense of human rights

17. What were the terms of the Panama Canal Treaty? It allowed for the joint American and
    Panamanian operation of the canal until the year 2000, when Panama assumed full control.

18. What was the peace agreement between Israel and Egypt called? Camp David Accords

19. What did Egypt agree to in those talks? Egypt agreed to peace and to recognize Israel's
    sovereignty as a nation.

20. What did Israel agree to? Israel agreed to return the Sinai Peninsula to Egypt.

21. Was the SALT II Treaty ever ratified? no

22. What action by the Soviets greatly affected the SALT II decision? The Soviet Union
    invaded Afghanistan and set up their own government leader.

23. What was the "Carter Doctrine"? the statement that the United States would resist by
    military force any Soviet attempt to push farther south to the Persian Gulf

24. Who was the Islamic extremist who denounced the United States as "the great Satan"?
    the Ayatollah Khomeini

25. Why did Iran take American hostages? because of American support of the former Shah

26. How many hostages were taken? fifty-three hostages

27. How many days did the Americans remain hostage? 444

28. Who campaigned against Carter for the Democratic nomination in the election of
    1980? Senator Edward Kennedy, the younger brother of John and Robert

29. What liberal Republican ran as an independent third-party candidate? John Anderson

30. Who won the presidential election of 1980? Ronald Reagan

SKILL: Recognition

Map Study: The Reagan Doctrine in Central America and the Caribbean

Refer to the map on page 625 of the text to complete the map below.

1. Label the following countries:

   Costa Rica   El Salvador   Guatemala   Nicaragua
   Cuba   Grenada   Panama

2. Use green to color the country that the United States helped with arms and advice and economic aid.

3. Use red to color the country that supplied arms to the Salvadoran rebels.

4. Use yellow to color the Caribbean country that, with the support of the Soviets, backed the Sandinista guerrillas.

5. If the Central American countries had fallen to communism, what strategic shipping lane may also have gone into Communist hands? _the Panama Canal_____

   Use blue to color it.

The First Four Years

Put the letter of the correct answer in the blank. Then answer the questions at the bottom of the page. Answers may be used once or more than once.

__B__ 1. Mujahideen

__K__ 2. tough stance against Communist aggression

__L__ 3. lower unemployment, interest, and oil prices

__A__ 4. Leon Klinghoffer killed

__F__ 5. automatic deficit reduction plan

__G__ 6. Maurice Bishop

__D__ 7. income tax cut 25% over $2\frac{1}{2}$ year period

__I__ 8. cut taxes and reduced government regulation

__E__ 9. Sandinistas vs. the Contras

__M__ 10. amount of proposed budget cuts

__H__ 11. PLO involvement

__C__ 12. Jonas Savimbi

__J__ 13. supply-side economics

__B__ 14. toy truck bombs

__N__ 15. amount of interest payments on debts

A. *Achille Lauro*
B. Afghanistan
C. Angola
D. Economic Recovery Tax Act
E. El Salvador
F. Gramm-Rudman Act
G. Grenada
H. Lebanon
I. limited-government agenda
J. Reagonomics
K. Reagan Doctrine
L. Roaring 80s
M. $35 billion
N. $150 billion

16. What problem caused the Gramm-Rudman Act to be less effective than it might have been? Congress exempted many programs from the Gramm-Rudman cuts. No one wanted his special interest group's budget cut.

17. What was the chemical weapon used in Afghanistan called? Yellow Rain

18. What event caused the United States peace-keeping forces to withdraw from Lebanon? On October 23, 1983, a terrorist drove a bomb-laden truck into the U.S. Marine barracks, killing 241 Americans.

19. Explain supply-side economics in your own words. Answers will vary. The students should see that supply-side economics increases the supply of goods to drive costs down, which, in turn, allows the consumer to buy more and thereby increases demand and causes manufacturers to increase production, allowing for more hiring.

20. What were the two points of the Reagan Revolution? (1) America must be strong. (2) America must be free.

21. In spite of all the budget cut demands, what area received a boost in spending, and how much money did it receive? Defense spending was increased by $12 billion.

This or That

Underline the choice that will make the statement correct.

1. Hungary / <u>Poland</u> was the first Communist-bloc country to open the way for free elections.

2. Geraldine Ferraro was the first woman <u>vice-presidential candidate</u> / appointed to the Supreme Court.

3. *Glasnost* / *Perestroika* gave the Russians a thirst for freedom and renewed nationalism.

4. INF / <u>SDI</u> / START was a proposed space-based defense system.

5. <u>The "Reagan Revolution"</u> / Reaganomics had two points stating that America must be strong and free.

6. The <u>INF treaty</u> / START agreement eliminated most medium-range missiles from Europe.

7. President Reagan began funneling supplies to <u>Angola</u> / Grenada to aid in stopping Cuban and Soviet influence.

8. When it opened its western borders, <u>Hungary</u> / Poland became an escape route for East Germans and Rumanians.

9. The meetings between the Soviet Union and the United States to cut the size of long-range nuclear arsenals were called INF / <u>START</u> / SDI.

10. The Mujahideen were guerrilla forces the Soviets tried to stop in Iraq / <u>Afghanistan</u>.

11. Reagan's second-term election was a <u>49 to 1</u> / 28 to 22 state victory.

12. <u>Qaddafi</u> / Khomeini, leader of Libya, was surprised when the United States responded to his support of terrorism with air strikes.

13. The undercover use of money from the sale of arms to aid in the battle against the Communist Sandinistas became the object of an investigation into Just Cause / <u>the Iran-Contra affair</u>.

14. The focus of Reagan's second term was on <u>foreign</u> / domestic affairs.

15. John Poindexter's / <u>Oliver North's</u> indictment in the Iran-Contra affair was overturned in 1990.

16. On November 9, 1989, the Iron Curtain / <u>Berlin Wall</u> ceased to be a barrier and opened the way for German reunification.

17. *Glasnost* / *Perestroika* was the restructuring of the Communist economy.

18. The election of George Bush to the presidency was in many ways a last show of approval for <u>Ronald Reagan</u> / Dan Quayle.

19. The governor of Massachusetts, Jack Kemp / <u>Michael Dukakis</u>, ran against Bush in the 1988 election.

20. The Soviet head of state who brought *glasnost* to the Soviet society was Leonid Brezhnev / <u>Mikhail Gorbachev</u>.

Map Study: Operation Desert Storm

Refer to the map on page 635 of the text to complete the map below.

1. Label the following countries:
Egypt	Iran	Jordan	Lebanon	Syria
Iraq	Israel	Kuwait	Saudi Arabia	

2. Label the following cities:
Baghdad	Jerusalem	Tel Aviv
Cairo	Kuwait City	

3. Use red to color the country that Iraq invaded.

4. Why was this country worth going to war over? _because of its large oil resources_

——————————————————————————————————

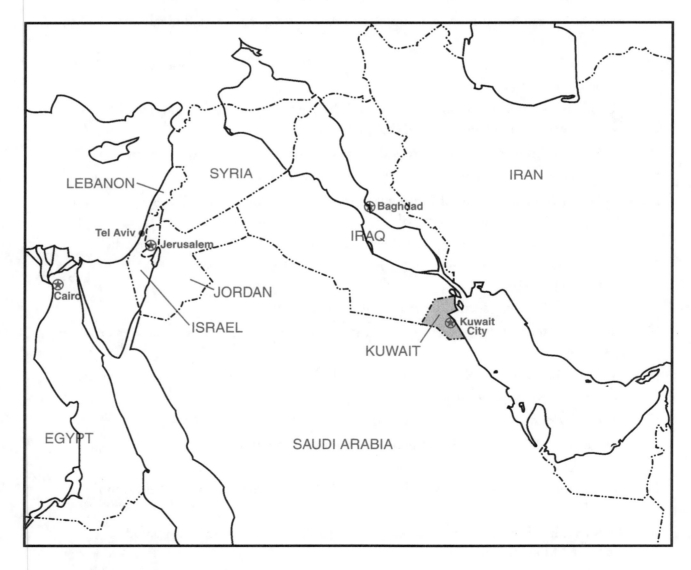

SKILL: Maps

The Gulf War Presidential Address

On Wednesday, January 16, 1991, President Bush addressed the nation concerning the bombing of Iraq. In his speech the president included the reasons for U.S. involvement and goals to be achieved. Read the excerpt from his speech and list his reasons and goals.

Five months ago, Saddam Hussein started this cruel war against Kuwait; tonight the battle has been joined. This military action, taken in accord with United Nations resolutions and with the consent of the United States Congress, follows months of constant and virtually endless diplomatic activity on the part of the United Nations, the United States and many, many other countries.

Arab leaders sought what became known as an Arab solution, only to conclude that Saddam Hussein was unwilling to leave Kuwait. Others traveled to Baghdad in a variety of efforts to restore peace and justice. Our Secretary of State, James Baker, held an historic meeting in Geneva only to be totally rebuffed.

Now, the 28 countries with forces in the gulf area have exhausted all reasonable efforts to reach a peaceful resolution, have no choice but to drive Saddam from Kuwait by force. We will not fail.

As I report to you, air attacks are under way against military targets in Iraq. We are determined to knock out Saddam Hussein's nuclear bomb potential. We will also destroy his chemical weapons facilities. Much of Saddam's artillery and tanks will be destroyed.

Our objectives are clear. Saddam Hussein's forces will leave Kuwait. The legitimate government of Kuwait will be restored to its rightful place, and Kuwait will once again be free.

Sanctions, though having some effect, showed no signs of accomplishing their objectives. Sanctions were tried for well over five months, and we and our allies concluded that sanctions alone would not force Saddam from Kuwait.

While the world waited, Saddam Hussein systematically raped, pillaged, and plundered a tiny nation—no threat to his own. He subjected the people of Kuwait to unspeakable atrocities, and among those maimed and murdered—innocent children. While the world waited, Saddam sought to add to the chemical weapons arsenal [that] he now possesses an infinitely more dangerous weapon of mass destruction, a nuclear weapon.

And while the world waited, while the world talked peace and withdrawal, Saddam Hussein dug in and moved massive forces into Kuwait. While the world waited, while Saddam stalled, more damage was being done to the fragile economies of the Third World, the emerging democracies of Eastern Europe, to the entire world, including to our own economy.

The United States, together with the United Nations, exhausted every means at our disposal to bring this crisis to a peaceful end.

I'm hopeful that this fighting will not go on for long and that casualties will be held to an absolute minimum. This is an historic moment. We have in this past year made great progress in ending the long era of conflict and Cold War. We have before us the opportunity to forge for ourselves and for future generations a new world order, a world where the rule of law, not the law of the jungle, governs the conduct of nations. When we are successful, and we will be, we have a real chance at this new world order, an order in which a credible United Nations can use its peacekeeping role to fulfill the promise and vision of the UN's founders.

It is my hope that somehow the Iraqi people can even now convince their dictator that he must lay down his arms, leave Kuwait, and let Iraq itself rejoin the family of peace-loving nations.

And let me say to everyone listening or watching tonight: When the troops we've sent in finish their work, I'm determined to bring them home as soon as possible. Tonight, as our forces fight, they and their families are in our prayers.

May God bless each and every one of them and the coalition forces at our side in the Gulf, and may He continue to bless our nation, the United States of America.

1. Reasons for: Saddam unwilling to leave Kuwait. No progress in getting him to leave. Sanctions showed no signs of accomplishing their objective. Saddam raped, pillaged, and plundered Kuwait, subjecting the people of Kuwait to unspeakable atrocities. Sought to increase his chemical arsenal and obtain a nuclear weapon. Damaged economies of Third World, emerging Eastern European democracies, the world, and the United States. All attempts to bring this crisis to a peaceful end had been exhausted.

_____

_____

_____

_____

_____

_____

_____

_____

_____

_____

_____

2. Goals: Knock out Saddam's nuclear bomb potential. Destroy his chemical weapons facilities. Destroy much of his artillery and tanks. Make Hussein's forces leave Kuwait. Restore rightful government to Kuwait and return its freedom. Forge for this and future generations a new world order in which the rule of law governs, with a credible United Nations as a peacekeeper. The Iraqi people will convince their dictator to lay down his arms and leave Kuwait so that Iraq can rejoin the family of peace-loving nations.

_____

_____

_____

_____

_____

_____

_____

_____

_____

_____

_____

Opposition and Support

As President Clinton began his first term in office, he initiated several policies. Chart the description of each policy and identify whether it was supported or opposed by Congress. The activity could be used in a class discussion that further explores reasons for the support or opposition of the policies.

Policy	Description	Supported/Opposed
"Don't Ask, Don't Tell"	Homosexuals in the military were not to declare their homosexuality, and no one was to ask them about it.	Opposed
Family and Medical Leave Act	Businesses were to give employees up to twelve weeks of unpaid leave to care for newborn children or seriously ill family members.	Supported
Brady Bill	Before a gun shop could sell a gun, there was a five-day waiting period and background check on the purchaser.	Supported
National Voter Registration Act	"Motor Voter Act" It required states to allow voters to register when they applied for or renewed a driver's license.	Supported
NAFTA	The North American Free Trade Act opened free trade with Mexico.	Supported
Health Care	Clinton promised universal insurance coverage—low medical care costs with taxes being raised to cover costs—which would create new government bureaucracy.	Opposed

Questions and Answers

Answer the following questions using the textbook and reference materials.

1. Why was President Clinton referred to as "the comeback kid"?

   In 1980 he was defeated in the Arkansas governor's race, but came back to win the office. Defeated

   in the 1992 New Hampshire presidential primary after sexual immorality allegations, he went on

   to win the Democratic nomination. Despite defeats on health care plan and congressional elections,

   he began another comeback.

2. Why did one Democratic congressman say that if a person did not like President Clinton's position on a particular issue, he needed only to wait a few weeks?

   Clinton would change policy according to public opinion. For example, when the public began

   to view Clinton as a liberal, he became a centrist.

3. How did signing the Defense of Marriage Act hurt Clinton's endorsement of homosexual rights?

   It denied any status to homosexual "unions" by securing federal benefits, such as health insurance,

   for spouses in traditional marriages only.

4. When and how did President Clinton present himself as a New Democrat?

   In Clinton's 1996 State of the Union Address, he stated his position as tough on crime, supportive

   of family values, and ready to reform welfare. He said, "The era of big government is over."

5. Why did the Supreme Court strike down the line-item veto?

   It would give too much power to the executive branch. A Constitutional amendment would be

   required for an all-inclusive line-item veto. The line-item veto could be overridden by a two-third's

   vote in both houses of Congress.

6. What negative character qualities do some of the previous questions' answers illustrate about President Clinton?

   sexual immorality allegations—low morals; no commitment—changed with what was popular;

   endorsed homosexual rights in spite of signing Marriage Act—not trustworthy—supported a sinful

   way of life

Dayton Accords

The following fundamental rights and freedoms are from the Dayton Peace Accords on Bosnia. Using the Declaration of Independence, the Bill of Rights, and Amendment 13 identify specific phrases that correspond to the Dayton Accords Rights and Freedoms.

Dayton Accords Rights and Freedoms

1. Right to life.— _Declaration—"Endowed by their Creator . . . these are life . . ."_

2. Right not to be subjected to torture or inhuman or degrading treatment or punishment.— _Amendment III—cruel, unusual, unjust punishments_

3. Right not to be held in slavery or servitude or to perform forced or compulsory labor.— _Amendment XIII—No slavery or involuntary servitude_

4. Rights to liberty and security of person.— _Declaration—". . . these are life, liberty, . . ."_

5. Right to a fair hearing in civil and criminal matters and other rights.— _Amendments VI and VII—Rights of the Accused in Criminal Trials and Rights of Citizens in Civil Trials_

6. Right to private and family life, home, and correspondence— _Amendment IX— Unspecified Rights_

7. Freedom of thought, conscience, and religion.— _Amendment I—Foundational Freedoms: Freedom of Speech and Freedom of Religion_

8. Freedom of expression.— _Amendment I—Foundational Freedoms: Freedom of Speech, Press, and to Petition Government_

9. Freedom of peaceful assembly and freedom of association with others.— _Amendment I—Foundational Freedoms: Freedom to Assemble_

10. Right to marry and to found a family.— _Amendment IX—Unspecified Rights_

11. Right to property.— _Amendment XIV—Citizenship Sec.1_

12. Right to education.— _Amendment IX—Unspecified Rights_

13. Right to liberty of movement and residence.— _Amendment IX—Unspecified Rights_

14. No discrimination on any grounds to prevent the enjoyment of the rights and freedoms.— <u>Declaration—". . . that all are endowed by their Creator with certain unalienable</u> <u>rights . . ."</u>

Discussion

1. List those freedoms or rights not specifically stated in the Declaration or Constitution:

   <u>Right to private and family life, home, and correspondence—Right to marry and found a family—</u>

   <u>Right to education—Right to liberty of movement and residence</u>

   _____

2. For class discussion:

   a) Why were the Dayton Accords so specific with regard to the rights and freedoms listed in the previous question?

   <u>Prior to World War I the peoples of this area enjoyed these freedoms and rights. Beginning in 1928</u>

   <u>and into the 1930s, extremists gained power. Hitler invaded and divided the country. Ethnic</u>

   <u>cleansing began to occur. Communist leader Tito took over after WWII. Freedoms and rights were</u>

   <u>limited. In 1990 Milosevic issued decrees curbing educational and political rights of ethnic</u>

   <u>minorities. After three years of warfare, the Dayton Accords were signed, specifically giving back</u>

   <u>these rights.</u>

   b) Why were some freedoms and rights not specifically stated in the U.S. Constitution?

   <u>As British citizens, the colonists had enjoyed these basic rights and freedoms. Answers will vary.</u>

   _____

   c) Which groups of people in the United States were not privileged to these specific rights prior to 1865?

   <u>The rights of slaves and, in certain areas of the United States, Native Americans were restricted.</u>

   _____

   d) Which freedom did the Proclamation Line of 1763 hinder? (See p. 97 of the text.)

   <u>Right to liberty of movement and residence</u>

   _____

Clinton Foreign Policy

Identify the countries in which President Clinton placed U.S. troops or maintained their presence in conjunction with his foreign policy. Chart the country, military involvement and reasons for being there, and the result.

Country	Military Involvement and Reasons	Result
Somalia	Troops there previously—sent in army specialists, Rangers, to track down Somali warlords	U.S. helicopter shot down—American soldier's body dragged through streets—American forces withdrawn
Haiti	Democratically elected president overthrown by military unit—pressure applied to Haitian regime to allow president to return to office—U.S. military threatened armed intervention	Haitian military backed down—president returned to office
Bosnia	Provided air support for United Nation's peace-keeping efforts—troops sent to keep peace	Uneasy peace—troops still there
Yugoslavia	Kosovar refugees and Serb government—brutal policies caused UN forces to be joined by U.S. forces to launch air strikes against Yugoslavian military and government targets	Yugoslavs gave in—NATO and Russian forces moved in—peace restored in Kosovo

What Do You Remember?

Identify each of the following.

_____Defense of Marriage Act_____   1. Secured federal benefits for spouses in traditional marriages only

_____"Contract with America"_____   2. Ten popular bills House Republicans promised to bring up for a vote

_____Christian Coalition_____   3. Conservative religious organization

_____line-item veto_____   4. Would allow the president to eliminate specific spending items in the federal budget

_____"Gay Rights" Movement_____   5. Rising political force seeking ways to secure legal recognition of the homosexual lifestyle

_____World Wide Web_____   6. Network of local servers connected electronically around the world

_____Lewinsky scandal_____   7. Event dominating the second term of President Clinton

_____Hillary Rodham Clinton_____   8. In charge of a task force to plan the best way to implement health care reform

_____"Whitewater" Scandal_____   9. Most significant scandal of the Clinton presidency; led to great humiliation in second term

_____Welfare Reform Act of 1996_____   10. Required welfare recipients to go back to work within two years; placed a lifetime cap of five years for assistance

_____Bob Dole_____   11. 1996 Republican presidential candidate

_____Internet_____   12. International network joining thousands of smaller networks into one

_____Dayton Accords_____   13. Agreement fashioning Bosnia into a confederation in which Serbs, Croats, and Muslims shared power

_____"talk radio"_____   14. New force in America by which conservative views on political issues were expressed

_____Kosovo_____   15. Yugoslavian province that became the scene of ethnic clashes

_____"The Comeback Kid"_____   16. Nickname of Bill Clinton reflecting his continued rebounding despite problems and scandals

_____NAFTA_____   17. Legislation opening free trade with Mexico

_____Somalia_____   18. Country whose warlords baffled President Clinton, leading to a withdrawal of U.S. troops

_____e-mail_____   19. Reduced normal correspondence and telephone calls

_____Chief Justice Rehnquist_____   20. Presided over the impeachment trial of President Clinton

_____Brady Bill_____   21. One of Congress's most significant pieces of gun control legislation

_____Focus on the Family_____   22. Conservative broadcast combining radio and religion

2001 Inaugural Address

After reading excerpts from President George W. Bush's inaugural address, explain what you think the president meant. Answers will vary. Activity could be used in a class discussion.

Excerpt 1:

We have a place, all of us, in a long story—a story we continue, but whose end we will not see. It is the story of a new world that became a friend and liberator of the old, a story of a slave-holding society that became a servant of freedom, the story of a power that went into the world to protect but not possess, to defend but not to conquer.

Possible meaning: All people in the U.S. have a place in U.S. history—the U.S. appreciated the old world

and brought liberty to it—once a slave-holding nation but now serves freedom—uses its power in the

world to defend and protect, not possess and conquer (history and foreign policy).

_____

_____

Excerpt 2:

Through much of the last century, America's faith in freedom and democracy was a rock in a raging sea. Now it is a seed upon the wind, taking root in many nations.

Possible meaning: The U.S. offers stability to a stormy world—faith in freedom and democracy is taking

root in many other nations (refers to America's world influence).

_____

_____

_____

Excerpt 3:

America has never been united by blood or birth or soil. We are bound by ideals that move us beyond our backgrounds, lift us above our interests and teach us what it means to be citizens. Every child must be taught these principles. Every citizen must uphold them. And every immigrant, by embracing these ideals, makes our country more, not less, American.

Possible meaning: Refers to America's immigrant beginnings. Ideals were the uniting factors—these ideals

were more important than where the people came from or their interests—these ideals teach us to be

citizens, and our children need to be taught these principles—immigrants should adopt these ideals that

encourage the American way of life (U.S. citizenship).

_____

Excerpt 4:

Our national courage has been clear in times of depression and war, when defending common dangers defined our common good. Now we must choose if the example of our fathers and mothers will inspire us or condemn us. We must show courage in a time of blessing by confronting problems instead of passing them on to future generations.

Possible meaning: Americans displayed courage in difficult times of war and depression—Americans

should choose to confront problems and not leave them for future generations to solve (American

responsibility).

Excerpt 5:

The enemies of liberty and our country should make no mistake: America remains engaged in the world by history and by choice, shaping a balance of power that favors freedom. We will defend our allies and our interests. We will show purpose without arrogance. We will meet aggression and bad faith with resolve and strength. And to all nations, we will speak for the values that gave our nation birth.

Possible meaning: Challenge to U.S. enemies—the U.S. will be on the side of freedom—will defend allies

and U.S. interests—U.S. attitude will not be one of arrogance but of strength and determination—will

support those values that created America (stance toward U.S. enemies).

Excerpt 6:

And whatever our views of its cause, we can agree that children at risk are not at fault. Abandonment and abuse are not acts of God, they are failures of love.

Possible meaning: Abandonment and abuse are not the fault of children or God—these are failures of love

(failure of parents).

Excerpt 7:

Government has great responsibilities for public safety and public health, for civil rights and common schools. Yet compassion is the work of a nation, not just a government.

Possible meaning: Government responsibilities of public safety, public health, civil rights, and common

schools are the responsibility of all citizens, not just government, and are motivated by compassion

(U.S. responsibilities and work).

Excerpt 8:

And I pledge our nation to a goal: When we see that wounded traveler on the road to Jericho, we will not pass to the other side.

Possible meaning: Nation's goal is illustrated in the biblical reference to the Good Samaritan. Help a person

in need—do not ignore (concern for the individual).

_____

_____

_____

Excerpt 9:

Our public interest depends on private character, on civic duty and family bonds and basic fairness, on uncounted, unhonored acts of decency which give direction to our freedom.

Possible meaning: What a person is in private makes a difference to the public as a whole—our freedoms

are affected by family, fairness, civic duty, and unknown acts of decency (private character matters).

_____

_____

_____

Excerpt 10:

I will live and lead by these principles: to advance my convictions with civility, to pursue the public interest with courage, to speak for greater justice and compassion, to call for responsibility and try to live it as well.

Possible meaning: Principles the president plans to live by—will promote what he thinks is correct in the

proper manner—will courageously do what is best for the people—will be vocal for more justice and

compassion—will encourage people to be responsible and will be responsible himself (presidential

principles).

Excerpt 11:

What you do is as important as anything government does. I ask you to seek a common good beyond your comfort; to defend needed reforms against easy attacks; to serve your nation, beginning with your neighbor. I ask you to be citizens: citizens, not spectators; citizens, not subjects; responsible citizens, building communities of service and a nation of character.

Possible meaning: Emphasizes individual responsibility—go beyond comfort zone for common good—

defend needed reform when attacked—serve your neighbor as a means of serving your country—be

citizens, not spectators or subjects—build communities that serve and build a nation with character

(focus on individuals making the difference).

_____

Excerpt 12:

After the Declaration of Independence was signed, Virginia statesman John Page wrote to Thomas Jefferson: "We know the race is not to the swift nor the battle to the strong. Do you not think an angel rides in the whirlwind and directs this storm?"

Possible meaning: We cannot depend on our own abilities. God's hand is on our nation, and He is

directing our nation (God's directing hand).

Excerpt 13:

We are not this story's author, who fills time and eternity with his purpose. Yet his purpose is achieved in our duty, and our duty is fulfilled in service to one another.

Possible meaning: The American story was begun not by individuals but by God, whose purposes direct

time and eternity. We achieve God's purpose by serving one another—could be alluding to Matthew 22:39,

"Thou shalt love thy neighbor as thyself" (service to God and others).

Excerpt 14:

Never tiring, never yielding, never finishing, we renew that purpose today, to make our country more just and generous, to affirm the dignity of our lives and every life.

Possible meaning: It is those in America who persevere that make our country more just and generous.

Reminds us of our personal dignity and the dignity of every life (individual dignity).

Excerpt 15:

This work continues. This story goes on. And an angel still rides in the whirlwind and directs the storm. God bless you all, and God bless America.

Possible meaning: The work of each individual continues as does our history as a nation—God still

directs our path—Asks for God's blessings on us as individuals and as a nation (final words).

SKILL: Analysis